# BARKING MAD!

## Confessions of a Dog-Sitter
## by Jane Mosse

2020

Published by Blue Ormer Publishing
for Bordeaux Barn Writers.
www.blueormer.co.uk

ISBN 978-1-9993415-2-7 (paperback)
ISBN 978-1-9993415-6-5 (e-book)

*For Eddie, Scheggia and Charlie,*
*where it all began.*

# PRELUDE

'You're going to do what?' asked my brother one evening during our monthly phone call.

'We're going to take up house-sitting.'

'If it's not a silly question, why?'

'Well, we miss not having a dog around and we don't want the commitment or the heartache of having another one. This way we can have a furry friend or two and explore pastures new.'

'So how much are you going to get paid?'

'We're not, we don't want to get paid. It's all done on trust and we prefer it that way. We get to stay in some wonderful houses, meet some lovely people and enjoy the company of their animals. All we have to do is get ourselves there.'

'So you mean it's another of your crack-pot ideas. You're mad. Barking mad.'

# 1

# BARKING MAD

'I WISH HE WOULDN'T do that,' says Rob, resting his knife and fork on the sides of his plate.

'Do what darling?'

'Stare at me while I'm eating and look miserable. It makes me feel guilty.'

'Well so it should. You're having chicken and bacon and he's getting dry biscuits. He's entitled to look miserable,' I reply.

Eddie is sitting at the kitchen table. What makes this somewhat unnerving is that Eddie is a dog. A beagle. Eddie the Beagle. Actually we're not all that sure about the beagle bit because Eddie is blonde with no splodges.

'You know Chris, I'm not at all convinced he is a beagle,' says Rob staring studiously at our new furry friend. 'I mean beagles are supposed to have black and tan markings. He just looks like a lab puppy with short legs.'

'Well I'm sure that remark would endear us to Ludovica and Jeremy,' I reply. 'We can hardly challenge them on the pedigree of their dog when we've only just met them, now can we?'

I'd seen the couple's advert for housesitters on the web-site that we'd recently subscribed to. Initially I hadn't paid it much attention as the main reason for getting into housesitting was to travel and explore pastures new. The company that we'd just signed up to advertised glamorous houses and adorable animals all over the world. We could visit Canada, Costa Rica, Tuscany or even China to look after a labradoodle, a donkey, some tropical fish or even a field full of alpacas, but here we were, still at home in Guernsey, about to drive four miles up the road to care for a couple of dogs and a cat. I realised that it was rather near to home but reasoned with Rob that, being so close, we could always pop back to keep an eye on our place and it would give us the opportunity to see if we were cut out for this sort of thing. Rob agreed with my thinking and suggested I apply.

A few days and a cup of coffee later and we'd been invited to take over the household while Ludovica and Jeremy went away for a long weekend to go caving. And so we found ourselves sitting at the kitchen table being eye-balled by Eddie who had taken up his apparently, customary position on the chair at the end of the table.

'Why on earth does anyone want to go caving?' asks Rob. 'The idea of being underground and squeezing through those tiny gaps while being dripped on would terrify me. I mean what if you got trapped?'

'Well clearly it's something they want to try but I have to confess I'd be terrified too. Still, each to his own. It's clearly something that excites the pair of them.'

Eddie is a typical beagle (in spite of looking like a labrador) whose whole life revolves around food. He manages to bolt down his two meals a day in seconds and is also a dab hand at helping with the pre-wash when the plates get stacked in the dishwasher. If he could climb inside I'm sure he would. Although we've been told that he's going deaf he still manages to hear the fridge door open from two rooms away. Pick up a packet of crisps and he's by your side looking imploringly at you in seconds.

He's very much a laid-back sort of dog, especially compared to his buddy Scheggia (that's Italian, like her owner). Scheggia, pronounced Skeja, is a Parson's Jack Russell. I'd never heard of the Parson's bit before I met Scheggy. They have hairy beards which don't look quite right on a female dog. She's typical of her breed: bouncy, nosey and bossy. Although Eddie's decidedly bigger than his sister it's she who rules the roost. The moment the poor fellow's tail's turned she leaps into his bed then watches smugly as he begrudgingly tries to fit his huge bulk into her tiny basket.

Sometimes, just for a change, Scheggia likes to take over the cat's bed. Charlie, the Burmese cat, is less put out than Eddie as he's able to seek other comfortable accommodation around the kitchen. The window-sill offers a magnificent view over the sea to the neighbouring islands and the sun tends to linger there for much of the day. His chocolate-brown coat absorbs the rays as he sits contentedly, singeing in the heat. Eddie also likes to be comfortable but his favourite spot for relaxation is, alarmingly, on top of the kitchen table. Leave the room for more than a few moments and Eddie will have managed to move one of the heavy, oak kitchen chairs and will be stretched out on top of the table snoring. This results in our having to wipe down the table before every meal in order to remove the thin coating of white hairs that have irritatingly parted company from him. After only a couple of hours in his presence my black leggings have turned a mysterious shade of grey and I look as though I should be heading to the nearest beauty salon for a quick waxing. This is obviously one of the minuses of owning a beagle. They shed. The kitchen floor has a misty cloud of fur all over it and, in places, Eddie's hair is drifting around like the balls of tumble-weed that you see in American movies. Fortunately the cleaners are due tomorrow.

Our new friend, Ludovica, is slim, super-fit and attractive. Rob had commented on these facts at our first meeting as she sprinted easily down the drive to meet us wearing a pair of skinny jeans and a white, linen shirt that highlighted her tan. (If you sense a hint of envy then you're right). I realise that the personal gym in the basement could be the key to Ludovica's toned body. Just looking at it terrifies me (the gym, that is, not her body). The very smell of a leisure centre still makes my stomach heave in spite of the fact that I was once an aerobics instructor in the 70s when we all wanted to look like Jane Fonda. I became wary of exercise once my knees and back started to tell me it was a bad idea. I close the gym door and head back upstairs to the kitchen where I feel much more at ease.

Other people's kitchens are never straightforward. They rarely seem to keep things in the right place. It's Jeremy who appears to be in charge of the kitchen. I surmise this by the fact that the crockery is kept in a cupboard that's above the built-in oven and thus sits at least eighteen inches above my head. Ludovica is, like me, petite (or just short in my case) and I'm left wondering how she ever manages to reach the plates without standing on a chair.

The cookery book left open on the work-top is clearly meant for those who want to be lean and fit, but calls for numerous ingredients that I've never even heard of such as ras el hanout and za'atar. With gastric juices duly activated I head for the fridge and remove the stuffed pork fillet wrapped in bacon that I'd decided to treat us to and place it on the worktop. Needing to wash the knife I head for the sink. It's at this point that I hear a sudden thud and, turning round, witness Eddie removing a large piece of streaky bacon from around the pork fillet which has mysteriously found its way onto the floor.

'Eddie! You monster!' I bellow.

Although he looks suitably penitent it doesn't stop him from hastily wolfing down the rest of the bacon. I scoop up the pork before he manages to scoff the rest of our dinner and head for the sink to give it a good wash. This is not my normal practice but needs must.

So, having rescued what remains of the pork, Eddie and I end up careering around the island unit in the kitchen. The difficulty is that I actually find the whole event rather amusing but I'm determined not to let Eddie know. He eventually heads for his basket and lies down, head on paws, staring up at me sort-of apologetically.

Lesson learned. All food must be placed at the back of the work-surface out of Eddie's reach, as must Charlie's dish or Eddie will also eat the cat-food. Fortunately Scheggia's too small to reach anything so she remains beyond suspicion.

What one tends to forget is that cats can climb anywhere. Up curtains, up trees and, of course, easily onto a kitchen work surface. The next night it's Charlie's turn to be in trouble as I catch him with his head in the bowl of newly-grated Parmesan ready for the pasta. You literally can't turn your back for a moment in this house. In fact you can't even go to the loo while you're cooking without removing all foodstuffs from reach. And for those of us who have led fairly quiet, unadventurous lives, the smallest room in this house is guaranteed to make you feel like the most boring person on the planet.

'Rob, have you been in the downstairs loo yet?'

'No, why, is there something I'm missing?'

'Go and have a look, but I'll warn you, it's a bit deflating!'

A few minutes later Rob emerges looking decidedly dejected. The walls of the loo are bedecked with framed certificates which record that our super-fit householders are a couple of adrenalin junkies. Not only have they swum with sharks, been trekking for gorillas, looped the loop in a small aircraft and climbed Mount Kilimanjaro, they've jumped out of an aeroplane, run with the bulls in Pamplona and been to the North Pole. I'm suitably impressed and totally dispirited. My efforts at walking several marathons, piloting a small aircraft and flying on Concorde (oops, forgot that Jeremy's done that too) are now as nothing. I am an unadventurous wimp. This couple have clearly decided that if you don't get a certificate for something in life then it's not worth doing in the first place.

'See what I mean?' I remark.

'Mmm. I don't think we can compete with that lot. Mind you, I did get a medal for running the London Marathon once,' replies my man puffing out his chest at the memory. 'And I've got a Blue Peter badge.'

'Have you? You've never told me about that before. What was it for?'

'I submitted one of my first poems and I even appeared on the programme!' he replies proudly.

'Can you remember it?'

'Actually I can. It was called Penguins.

> *Penguins look like small fat men*
> *in dinner-suits awaiting lunch.*
> *They shuffle to and fro on ice,*
> *their webbed feet going crunch, crunch, crunch.'*

'Oh Rob that's brilliant! You were a talent even then. How old were you?'

'Nine I think. I've still got the badge somewhere.'

'Maybe you should wear it next time we see Jeremy and Ludovica and I'll wear my Concorde lapel brooch.'

Charlie has taken to Rob big time. After only twenty-four hours they can be found velcroed together or with Charlie helping Rob to work on his computer. Rob's always been a dog person but I suspect that Charlie's working his magic. He's a fragile little thing and a real feather-weight, gentle and affectionate. Sadly he's been diagnosed with a form of feline leukaemia and is being treated with steroids. As a result he needs to eat frequently and is understandably indulged with pieces of chicken or prawns, having turned his nose up at all the top brands of cat food. He comes and goes happily throughout the day letting himself in or out of the cat-flap. Fortunately the dogs can also use the cat-flap and are then able to wander freely around the garden with no means of escape. This is a joy when you know that you don't have to take them round the block in the pouring rain at 11 o'clock at night for a last pee before bed-time and also a relief as taking any strange dog for a walk, especially at night, can be fraught with difficulties. Rob knows this from experience.

'Do you remember that time you took Malcolm for a walk that day and nearly lost him?' I chuckle.

'Ha! How could I forget it?' laughs Rob.

It was a couple of years ago when Rob had agreed to help out one of our neighbours with her dog, Malcolm. Malcolm was a nervous boy, a rescue dog, so when walking him you had to be extra-vigilant, especially when meeting other dogs. He was also very wary of traffic. And people.

Having popped down the lane to walk Malcolm, Rob returned looking somewhat stressed and dishevelled. It turned out that Malcolm, who was being walked on an extending lead, had run round Rob in a panic having spotted another dog. Rob, now bound and tethered, promptly fell over onto the path while Malcolm managed to lunge forward, breaking his lead in the process, and headed for the other dog. Fortunately at this point he lost his bottle, but the owner of the dog, an elderly lady, was clearly very concerned about this poor man who had taken a nasty tumble. Needless to say, Rob was more concerned that she should grab hold of Malcolm, although Malcolm wasn't the sort of dog to be grabbed hold of. Fortunately the story had a happy ending as Malcolm was rescued and Rob emerged unhurt. However, when we related the story to his owner we couldn't resist embroidering the ending a little. I think it involved an attack on a passing policeman. Shame on us!

Walking Eddie and Scheggia is an art that we have yet to perfect. Our first venture turns into something akin to Maypole dancing as their leads became inextricably tangled. The pair of them lunge from one hedge to another leaving Rob and me in the middle of a rather complex and messy knot. Although Eddie has short legs he proves to be incredibly strong, dragging Rob through the beautifully manicured gardens in the area and disappearing into people's shrubberies. Bin night proves an absolute disaster and it takes us forever just to walk round the block as Eddie attempts to explore the contents of every black bag in the neighbourhood.

'So sorry!' I mouth to a lady who's looking at us from the window of her house as Eddie makes a bee-line for her bin.

She opens the window and, fortunately for us, seems to be okay about an out-of-control beagle rooting through her re-cycling.

'Oh, he's cute!' she calls down. 'Hello puppy! We used to have a lab just like him. How old is he?'

Rob explains that Eddie is no longer a puppy, nor is he a lab, but an eleven-year-old beagle. Our lady is clearly surprised and we can see the look of disbelief on her face as she closes the window.

'You see what I mean!' exclaims Rob. 'I told you he looked more like a lab. I reckon they were conned when they got him.'

When I wake early the following morning the bedroom is filled with the most wonderful golden light. As I prop myself up on my pillow to look out of the window the sun is rising behind the island of Herm and the view over the water looks positively Mediterranean. The house sits high above the cliff path with a magnificent view of the neighbouring islands. The sea is like silk and, as the sun rises, turns from fiery orange to soft pink. The gulls swoop below in the canopy of the pine trees and a small fishing-boat, bedecked with brightly-coloured floats, sails into the picture, heading out to the distant island of Sark.

'Oh Rob, wake up, you have to see this!' I say, nudging the dozy bundle next to me. 'Just look at the islands. Isn't it beautiful?'

A sleepy head appears from under the duvet and peers out at the view.

'Mmm. Lovely,' he replies, then promptly turns over and covers his head with the bed-clothes.

'It's mornings like this when you wonder why we want to go anywhere else. We're so lucky to live on the island,' I sigh, but a muffled snore is already emanating from Rob's pillow.

It's late that evening when I'm engrossed in tweeting and Rob is busy working on a new poem, that the most fearful yelps are heard coming from the garden below the house. It's already dark so I grab a torch and hurry down the steps into the garden to find out what's happening. To my horror Scheggia is looking like something out of a Dracula movie, her mouth and chest dripping with blood and her face full of spines. I scoop her up and head for the house while she continues to yelp and shake uncontrollably.

'Good grief, what on earth's she done?' asks Rob.

'I think she's just tried to say hello to a hedgehog by the look of her face.'

Closer examination reveals several spines stuck into Scheggia's face and muzzle. We wrap her in a towel and, while I keep her tucked tightly under my arm, Rob sets to work to remove the spines. She's as good as gold yet very frightened, but slowly and gently we manage to get the prickles out of her face. My worry is that she might have spines in her mouth which could become infected.

'You'll need to look in her mouth,' I tell Rob. 'If they've got jammed between her teeth or stuck in her palate she's in trouble.'

'And so will I be if I try sticking my fingers in her mouth!' he replies indignantly. 'You do it and I'll hold her, I'm stronger than you.'

'No, I'm okay,' I reply quickly. 'I can hold her and she loves you more than me so she'll let you do it.'

'If she bites me I'm going to blame you,' replies Rob.

Scheggia's a model patient. It's as though she knows that we're trying to help her and, without complaint, lets Rob stick his finger in her mouth and probe gently around.

'All seems okay if you ask me,' he says. 'Supervet's giving her the all clear.'

By the time we return to the house for a further sit, having passed the initiation test and been invited back for a second stay, Scheggia's become addicted to hunting these prickled delicacies.

'Don't forget to close the gate before you go to bed!' Jeremy reminds me as I drop the pair of them off at the airport.

It seems that Scheggia has recently made several more demented attacks similar to the one we witnessed, so Jeremy has erected a baby gate at the bottom of the steps leading down onto the lawned area where the hedgehogs roam. The gate seems a very sensible precaution and, hopefully, the obvious solution.

'So where are Jeremy and Lucrezia off to this time dare I ask?' questions Rob when I get back to the house.

'It's Ludovica not Lucrezia, and they're going bungee jumping in Switzerland,' I reply.

'What on earth do they want to do that for? They really are a couple of head-cases. No doubt they're paying for the pleasure of being scared witless. I don't know how they can even contemplate it, never mind do it. I'd be absolutely terrified.'

'Well you know me, I can't even walk across stepping stones without fear of dying. No amount of money could persuade me to do any of that sort of stuff,' I reply.

Later that evening I scuttle down the stairs and snap the latch on the garden gate firmly into place. Job done.

It's at precisely 2.20 a.m. that I'm woken by the sound of frantic barking coming from the garden. It sounds horribly like Scheggia. Rob is snoring peacefully so I quickly don a jumper and slip out into the night to find out what on earth's going on. Scheggia's at the bottom of the steps, her nose stuck firmly through the bars of the gate, barking into the darkness and obviously buzzing on adrenalin. She's clearly picked up on the scent or movement of the hedgehogs and is going demented. I scoop her up and carry her, struggling, back up the steps to the house. Our movement activates the security lighting and I suddenly find myself standing half-naked on the doorstep with a dog under my arm. I manage to open the door and scoot back into the kitchen where I return her to her bed while giving her a very firm warning of what I intend doing to her if she dares to repeat this dreadful display. Slipping back into the bedroom with goose-pimples on my goose-pimples I attempt to get warm again after my outing. Rob has by now slipped into one of his recurring dreams, most probably involving a car chase, and is squirming around the bed yanking the bed-clothes over to his side.

No sooner have I lain down than the noise starts again. The little madam has gone out through the dog-flap, back down the steps and her barking has become even more frenzied than before. I'm concerned that the neighbours aren't going to be too thrilled by this nocturnal recital. So, grabbing my coat, I run down the steps, lunge at her and, wrapping her tightly in my arms, carry her firmly back to her bed.

It seems that the only solution now is to block up the cat-flap to prevent her escaping. Several minutes later I've managed to haul one of the heavy, oak dining chairs over to the door, placed it on its side and leaned it up against the bread-board which is now firmly blocking the exit. Checking that Scheggia's now in her bed I head back to the bedroom and slide quietly between the sheets, frozen to the marrow, in the hope of warming up again and getting a night's sleep at long last.

Within minutes the barking starts again but, because she's now contained in the kitchen, (which is a large space with little in the way of soft furnishing) the noise is amplified hugely. I lie back in the dark wondering what on earth I can do to shut her up. I'm loath to let her come onto the bed as that could create a precedent. Rob continues to snore. Scheggia continues to bark and I continue to think I'm going to murder either one or both of them before the night is over.

And then the idea dawns on me. Eddie's squirty collar! Eddie has a nasty habit of waking us at about 6 a.m. when he's decided he'd like some breakfast. One bark and his squirty collar gives him a swift spray of citronella and he shuts up. Donning my jumper yet again I creep out of bed and make my way into the kitchen to Eddie's bed. He too is snoring. Carefully I manage to unclip his collar without waking him, adjust it slightly and clip it firmly round Scheggia's neck. She's shut up since my arrival in the kitchen but I'm not convinced by the silence.

For the third time I return to bed where my man is still in the land of nod. It's now 4.50 a.m. A loud bark resounds from the kitchen. But it is only one bark. Half an hour later yet another single bark is heard. And there it ends. Peace at last.

At six o'clock I'm woken by Rob who's thoughtfully brought me a cup of tea in bed. I could cheerfully murder him.

'Sorry it's so early love but Eddie just woke me up howling. He's a pain. I don't think that collar thing that he wears can be working. Did you have a good night? I must admit it's the best night's sleep I've had in a long time.'

Later that morning Ludovica and Jeremy return from the airport looking refreshed. I feel totally wrecked and, having checked in the bathroom mirror before going to greet them, notice that I have dark grey bags under my eyes.

'How was the flight back?' I ask, knowing that travel between the island and the mainland can be fraught with problems.

'It was wonderful!' squeals Ludovica excitedly. 'We got hit by lightning twice, it was so exciting! Some of the passengers were even screaming', she laughs. 'Anyhow, you guys. How's it been? Was everything okay?'

'Absolutely,' says Rob smiling a little too eagerly at her. 'We've had a really relaxed time, thanks, haven't we Chris? It's been a real pleasure.'

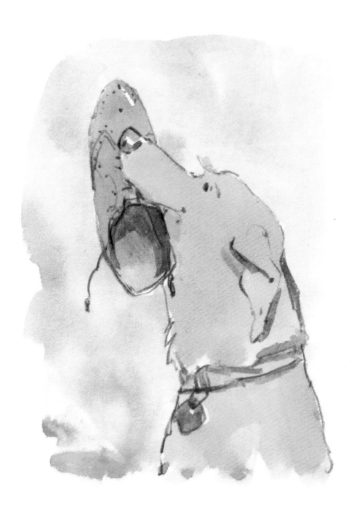

# 2

# LONDON PRIDE

ONE OF THE GROUND RULES we established when we first started house-sitting was that the accommodation had to be at least as good as home, if not better. This had always been our base-line for holidays and it seemed only sensible to apply it to house-sits. Not that home is particularly upmarket or glamorous, but we do like to be comfortable and surrounded by nice things. Hence we found ourselves rather cheekily applying for a sit in a rather elegant residence in London's Mayfair.

'We'll never get it,' moaned Rob. 'There'll be loads of people applying.'

'Why shouldn't we?' I replied defensively. 'We've got a string of five-star reviews behind us and for once age is on our side. We're mature and reliable, what more can anyone want?'

Humphrey, a handsome, russet-coloured, wire-haired Vizsla with doleful eyes and long, gangly legs, is at the gate to greet us, doing what can only be described as a happy dance. With his bottom planted firmly on the ground he rears up into the air with his front half and bounces excitedly on the spot. It's love at first sight. Or rather Humphrey has fallen for me big time. He thrusts a wet nose into my hand and then determinedly into my crotch. It's at this point that a rather dashing, but hugely embarrassed owner appears at the front door of the house.

'Humphrey!' he bellows and Humphrey dutifully slouches off into the hallway. 'I am so sorry, Humph's rather an affectionate fellow. I'm Jonathan, so pleased to meet you, do come in.'

The hallway of this place is big enough to swallow up the whole of the humble little cottage that we call home. Empty, apart from a red velvet chaise-longue and a huge, elliptical staircase that winds its way gracefully up from the ground floor past stylish niches displaying modern ceramics. The whole space is covered with a rich, soft gold carpet that looks as though it was fitted only yesterday and I immediately become conscious of not having removed my shoes on entering. Light floods in from a long window on the landing and bounces off a series of mirrors that adorn the adjoining wall and reflect the somewhat garish, yet totally fitting, chandelier. Our numerous stays in Venice tell me that it's all Murano glass.

'Gosh, it's stunning!' I gasp, 'You have a beautiful home.'

'Thank you, but it's all James' work. I leave it all to him,' replies Jonathan smiling.

At this moment an equally handsome young man, probably in his thirties, who we can only assume is James, appears from the back of the house. He looks as though he's stepped out of one of the Gieves and Hawkes catalogues that arrive regularly for Rob, except Rob just sighs longingly over the contents and then discards them. We introduce ourselves, make the usual small talk before being shown to our room on the first floor.

'We thought we'd put you in here if that's okay?' asks James. 'It overlooks the garden at the back so it'll be nice and quiet.'

The room is decorated entirely in black, white and gold, the sort of room that's featured in the glossy pages of *The Telegraph* supplement or *Tatler* magazine. A long settee upholstered in broad, black and white stripes, studded with brass buttons takes up one of the walls but the *pièce de resistance* is the bed. A huge, Napoleonic four-poster that dominates the room, the canopy supported by fluted, gold posts and swathed in black silk curtains, held in place by gold tie-backs with heavy, fringed tassels. The black silk shades of the bedside lamps are trimmed with black feathers and there's an unmistakable air of opulence all around. I can see the wide smile on Rob's face as he claps eyes on the Italianate marble bathroom complete with a huge, walk-in shower. Toiletries have been arranged on the black towels and two black, silk kimonos embroidered with gold dragons hang on the ornate, gold hooks on the back of the door. This place really does have the wow factor. We abandon our cases, hang up our coats in the wardrobe and follow James back downstairs to the kitchen.

'Martini?' says Jonathan handing us each a glass. 'Cheers and nice to meet you at last!'

I'm still trying hard not to let my jaw remain permanently dropped.

'Cheers, and thank you both for having us,' replies Rob as we all chink glasses.

Humphrey has returned to my side and is gazing wistfully up at me, drooling slightly. I bend over to stroke his head and he gives me a totally besotted look.

'I think you've found a friend!' says Jonathan.

I'm just praying that we don't have a repeat of the head between the legs bit when I realise that we haven't yet met our other charges.

'So where's Maisy?' I ask, looking around the room.

'Oh gosh, Maisy! Of course,' replies James. 'She'll be asleep in the lounge. I'll just go and get her.'

A couple of minutes later he returns with a very sleepy, slightly bald, grey bundle cradled carefully in his arms: a miniature and very elderly Schnauzer. My on-line investigations before we left have confirmed my suspicions that all Schnauzers have permanently grumpy faces and Maisy is no exception. Her face seems to wear a permanent frown. Her eye-brows meet in the middle of her forehead making her look as though she's scowling.

'She's totally deaf and almost blind I'm afraid,' says James, kissing the back of her head, 'and she's not too happy about being picked up. You'll need to approach her very carefully and give her plenty of time to know that you're there.'

Rob holds his hand close to Maisy's nose so that she can pick up on his scent and then, very gently, strokes her head.

'There,' James says to her. 'Uncle Rob and Aunty Christine are going to look after you while we're away.'

'So, are you two going somewhere exciting?' I ask, curious to know.

'Mmmm,' replies Jonathan between sips of martini. 'A couple of friends are getting married in Havana. There's a whole crowd going over so it should be fun.'

It's at this point that an extremely glamorous cat sashays into the kitchen and walks up to her dish (a silver dish that resembles a crown). Jonathan deftly bends down and scoops her up.

'And this lovely princess is Tallulah!' he cries. 'Hello my lovely Lula, come and say hello to Uncle Rob and Aunty Christine.'

Lula is a Maine Coon, soft, silky and glamorous. Her long apricot-coloured fur is groomed to perfection and her tail stands proud behind her like a luxurious feather-duster. She stretches out in Jonathan's arms until he nearly drops her.

'She's spoilt rotten I'm afraid. We've given up on tins and those sachet things so she only gets fish that we cook freshly each morning.'

I can feel my stomach heave at the very thought. I'm not a great fish cook but the idea of cooking it before breakfast is already making me feel nauseous.

'I've left all the instructions for you so don't worry.'

'And what about the other two?' I ask.

'Well Maisy's happy to have fish too but she does like a few mixed veg and some rice with it. I've bagged some stuff up ready for you and it's all in the freezer. It'll just need a quick blast in the microwave. Humph tends to have either spit-roast chicken or liver but he does like it pink, just flash-fried really. Harrods deliver his food Wednesday morning and Saturday if that's not inconvenient for you?'

'No, that's absolutely fine,' I reply.

Good grief, this lot eat better than we do. It sounds more like my idea of Hell's Kitchen at every turn.

'Any medication?' I add.

'Oh, gosh yes. I'm glad you mentioned it,' replies Jonathan. 'Lula needs a squirt of oil on her food, there's a bottle next to her grooming kit, it helps her coat to stay glossy, and we've been trying to get Maisy to take a turmeric tablet to help her joints but she's not at all keen is she James?'

'If you can manage to get a tablet down her you're doing better than we are!' replies James.

The next day, Louis Vuitton bags packed safely in the boot of the Jag, passports and pesos in their man-bags, the boys bid us all a fond farewell and head off to the airport. The moment they've gone Humphrey is by my side with a shoe in his mouth, a smart Church's brogue.

'Aw, thank you Humphrey. Is that for me?'

He's ecstatic and moves so close to me that he could be glued to my leg.

'I think I'm beginning to understand why they call them Velcro Vizslas,' I laugh.

'Well, he's certainly taken to you big time,' replies Rob. 'You're leading one-love.'

The scoring thing is something that started off quite early in our house-sitting history when we realised that the animals that we were looking after tended to bond more strongly with one or the other of us. Rob was winning on the cat-front but we were neck and neck with the dogs. I remember the breed characteristics that I'd read on-line and printed out for reference.

'Here Rob. Listen to this,' and I reach into my bag, fish out my notes and read:

*This breed is often described as the Velcro Vizsla. Most dogs are affectionate, but this medium-size hunting dog becomes very attached to his people. His Velcro nature has to do with his past: the Vizsla was raised to be both a pointer and retriever who worked close to the hunter, never moving far away. This trait is still seen in today's Vizsla, who prefers to be leaning against your leg or serving as a foot warmer. If having a dog shadow you all day would irritate you, choose a different breed.*

'Ha! Bit late now!' laughs Rob as Humphrey lies down on the kitchen floor, his front half carefully draped over my foot.

I'm up early the next morning, 7.15 to be precise, standing over a pan of liver and another of fish, trying hard not to retch. Humphrey is already into verse two of his happy dance staring longingly up at me, Lula is meowing loudly and rubbing herself up against my legs, Maisy is standing staring at a wall and Rob is still upstairs lying in state and snoring. I decide that wrapping a tea-towel round my face might help to mask the foul smells exuding from the delicacies cooking on the Aga. I line up the dishes on the work-top and dutifully spoon out the rations for our new furry friends. A quick squirt of oil for Tallulah and a cleverly disguised turmeric tablet for Maisy. I reckon a piece of ham carefully wrapped round the offending tablet will be enough to get the pill down her throat.

Within a matter of what seems like seconds all three bowls are empty. My twenty-odd minutes of hard labour have been rewarded by three clean plates and the return of a turmeric tablet that is balanced pointedly on the side of Maisy's dish. Damn! Little madam. Better luck next time.

After our own meagre breakfast of muesli and yoghurt we decide to brave our first walk with the dogs. Humphrey is in happy dance overdrive and Maisy is still staring at the wall. So, with leads firmly attached, intruder alarm set, we head off to explore.

I've only once strayed into Mayfair and that was when I

found myself hopelessly lost having walked out of Hyde Park in the wrong direction. It's a part of London that has wealth printed all over it. Elegant houses, imposing architecture and green spaces where you can escape the claustrophobic nature of the city and breathe. Our new home is just around the corner from Grosvenor Square and consequently only a couple of minutes from Hyde Park. Humphrey is clearly up for a good romp while dear Maisy stumbles along, unsure of her footing and relying heavily on the gentle pull of the lead to guide her. It's a bit of a mis-match trying to walk both dogs at the same time.

We'd agreed a policy of never letting a new dog off the lead for at least a day until we were confident that they were going to come back when called, so poor Humphrey is chomping at the bit to be given his freedom. However, there's no way that we can let go of Maisy considering her disabilities, so my dear Humphrey is going to have to put up with being dragged around for the rest of the day. Hyde Park is full of dogs running freely and I very soon sense that my new friend is not at all pleased with the new regime.

The next morning we decide that a better plan would be to walk the two dogs separately so that they can each go at their own pace; dear Maisy will then be able to plod along sedately and avoid bumping into stray lamp-posts, while Humphrey will be free to chase his ball which, we've been told, is his absolute favourite pastime. As Humphrey is very clearly my dog we agree that Rob will walk Maisy and I'll take my boy out for a good run.

And so I set off with my handsome, new friend in the direction of Hyde Park, Humphrey proudly carrying his ball in his mouth. I get slightly confused at one turning and end up walking past The Dorchester where a coach-load of Chinese visitors is being off-loaded onto the pavement before being escorted into the hotel. Several of them look in our direction with very wary expressions on their faces but one young lady bravely approaches and hesitantly asks in English if she might touch my dog.

'Of course,' I reply. 'He's very friendly.'

She leans forward gingerly and reaches out her hand to touch Humphrey's head. She reminds me of a visitor in an art gallery who's desperate to touch one of the exhibits but knows they'll be in trouble if they do. As she leans forward to pat Humphrey her fellow compatriots emit a united shriek and cower back against the wall of the hotel, hands raised in horror. Poor Humphrey is somewhat alarmed by their response and drops his ball in surprise. I quickly retrieve it and stick it back in his mouth while the visitors cry out in horror yet again. Somewhat bemused by their reaction I pull gently on the lead and Humphrey and I head off to the park to play ball.

After a dizzy half hour of Humph careering manically round the park I decide it's time to head for home and so, carefully avoiding the Dorchester, we wander back, Humphrey dutifully carrying his ball in his mouth which makes him look as though he has a huge smile on his face. His lovely red coat looks stunning in the sunshine and as we walk he occasionally tilts his head and looks up at me as if to check that I'm still there. This love is quickly becoming a two-way thing.

We haven't been home long when suddenly the back door flies open and, whooooosh, in flies Maisy like a bat out of hell, legs splayed, and skids alarmingly across the parquet floor. Both Humphrey and I jump back in alarm. Wherever has this new lease of life come from? This is a dog who could hardly walk unassisted only a matter of a couple of hours ago. It's only when I compose myself that I notice that she's covered with blood. My first thought is that she's been attacked, so when Rob flies through the door in hot pursuit I'm already imagining the worst.

'Oh my God, whatever's happened? Has something attacked her?'

I quickly grab the kitchen towel and try to catch her but she's having none of it and runs around frantically bumping into walls and pieces of furniture.

'Oh gosh, she's a real mess. Goodness knows how we're going to clean her up,' I cry.

'She's a mess?' explodes Rob. 'She's a mess? What about the mess she's made of my thumb?' he yells, holding his hand aloft. 'It was me who was attacked, not her. She bit me!' he shouts.

By now the kitchen floor is splattered with blood and it's only on looking back up at Rob that I realise that most of it's coming from his hand. I'm finding it difficult to piece this story together.

'Here, come and sit down and tell me exactly what happened while I sort you out,' I say quietly, hoping that my soothing tones will calm his hysteria while searching for something to tie round his hand.

He's visibly shaken and there really is a lot of blood escaping from his wound. The cuff of his shirt has become soaked and has turned a nasty shade of maroon.

'We set off for our walk and I'd had trouble with that damned chain on her lead, it just didn't seem to fit properly,' he gabbles. 'Anyhow, I started walking down the path, but when I opened the gate she suddenly darted straight past me out onto the road. She must have slipped the chain. I was terrified she was going to get run over so I grabbed her and of course she got frightened and turned round and bit me. I didn't dare let her go so I took hold of her back end so that she couldn't reach me with her teeth, ran back up the path and shoved her through the door.'

Poor Rob. He's clearly in a bad way and his hand needs attention. Meanwhile Maisy is standing shaking in the middle of the kitchen, her grey fur stained dark red all down one side of her back.

'Goodness knows how we're going to get that off her if she doesn't want to be touched,' I muse. 'We'll just have to hope that it falls off when it dries.'

'Yes, and we'll just have to hope that my thumb doesn't fall off too,' grumbles Rob looking decidedly sorry for himself. 'It's really nasty. It'll probably become infected and turn septic,' he adds dramatically.

Fortunately I recall having seen a first aid kit in the utility room so, trying to remember my Girl Guide first aid training, I bandage Rob's hand then track down a mop and bucket and manage to remove the blood trail from the kitchen floor.

'Thank goodness it was just the kitchen,' I sigh. 'Imagine if it had been all over the gold carpet.'

At feeding time that evening I search for something to disguise Maisy's tablet and find an already opened packet of San Daniele prosciutto at the back of the fridge. I cut off a small strip and wrap it carefully round the turmeric tablet. Ten minutes later her bowl is empty and there's no evidence of her having deposited it back in her dish. I check underneath her bowl and in the immediate area. Success! You owe me one James!

It's only on coming downstairs the following morning, sporting my black silk kimono and bracing myself for the culinary experience that awaits me, that I narrowly avoid stepping on a strange lump at the bottom of the stairs. At first I can't work out what on earth it is and then realise, to my horror, that it's the regurgitated contents of Maisy's stomach, all appropriately faded to the same colour as the new carpet.

I look aghast at the festering heap. Clearly the turmeric tablet has upset her system. My immediate reaction is to run and grab a wet cloth but I realise, just before springing into action, that this is the worst thing I can possibly do as any contact with water will turn the turmeric an alarming shade of yellow and stain the carpet irreparably. I try to put my brain into gear, a challenge at such an early hour in the morning, and then realise that the best approach is to try to remove the drying mass by scraping it off the pile of the carpet.

After rummaging around in several kitchen drawers and

cupboards I discover a large carving knife and a bowl, return to the hall and get down on my hands and knees. Carefully guiding the blade under the pile of vomit I scoop it deftly into the bowl, somehow managing to avoid staining my glamorous kimono.

It's at this moment that I hear the bedroom door open and a bleary-eyed Rob appears at the top of the stairs. He looks down on the scene; his wife sprawled out centre stage on the hall floor clutching a large knife.

'Good grief! It's like a scene from Madame Butterfly,' he chortles. 'What on earth are you doing darling?'

'I can't take any more of this standing over a pan full of raw liver first thing in the morning. I'm going to end it,' I wail.

'Gosh, if I'd known it was that bad I'd have offered to take over,' Rob hoots. 'Seriously sweetheart, why are you kneeling on the floor clutching a large carving knife?'

I explain the events of my morning, fortunately now able to see the funny side of the drama.

'I think you owe me a very large cup of strong coffee, preferably with a shot of brandy in it!'


The following day brings with it hours of torrential rain. It's days like this when you realise that having a dog to walk is absolutely no fun at all. Tallulah has been keeping a low profile and is lying spread-eagled across a sheepskin rug which is draped over the seat of a rather stylish rocking-chair. Her silky, apricot fur makes her look every inch the pedigree and she knows it. This is the sort of cat that would admire herself in the mirror at every opportunity were she human. She stares at me intently then stretches herself out to her full extent until she slides, unexpectedly, off the chair and ends up in an undignified heap on the floor. We can't help but laugh at her, at which point she strides determinedly to the door that leads out into the back garden.

'Meow,' she cries. 'Meow, meow, me-ow!'

I realise that this is why we talk about cats having staff rather than owners. She's beginning to sound rather impatient and glances over her shoulder at us with an aloof expression on her face.

'I guess she wants to go out. I've noticed she doesn't like using her litter tray,' I say and head for the patio door which I open into the driving rain.

'MEOW!' shrieks Lula, turns on her paws and dives under the table where only the plume of her tail can be seen thrashing from side to side.

'I guess that means she doesn't do rain either!' jokes Rob and heads off to the bathroom singing to himself, 'Her name was Lula, she was a show-girl...'

My relationship with Humphrey is now such that we are inseparable. If Rob and I go out and have to leave him for even a few minutes he greets me lovingly with a gift when we return: a shoe, a tea-towel, a sock, a cushion, in fact anything that he can wrap his jaws around. Even if I go to the loo Humphrey is outside the door whimpering and, on occasions, in the loo with me. I happen to be one of those people who considers visiting the bathroom a private matter, so to have a dog sitting staring avidly at me whilst I'm perched on the throne is somewhat unnerving.

'Humphrey, go away!' I command. 'Out! Shoo!'

He tilts his head to one side and looks offended then walks across the room and returns with a towel in his mouth.

'Give!' I say firmly.

But Humphrey doesn't respond, instead he sees this as an opportunity to play tug. I grab hold of my end of the towel and pull firmly making growling noises. How can you not love this dog?

Our last morning arrives and, having decided to reward myself with a lie-in, Rob kindly ventures downstairs to make me a cup of tea. Bliss! Except he leaves the kitchen door open and, before you know it, Humphrey is beside me with his dog-bed in his mouth.

'Oh Humph, you are a sweetheart but you know you're not allowed upstairs now go on, down!'

Humphrey does that head on the side thing and looks wounded.

'No Humphrey! Down! Downstairs!'

He doesn't move an inch so I climb out of bed, grab hold of his collar and lead him to the top of the stairs.

'Go on,' I say firmly, pointing in the direction of the kitchen. 'Down!'

Eager to obey, but not wanting to be parted from me, Humphrey launches himself off the top step, still with his bedding in his mouth. This somewhat large, padded cushion begins the downhill journey slightly ahead of him but, catching on the stairs, folds neatly back under his floundering bulk. The result is that Humphrey descends the stairs sitting on his cushion just as Rob exits the kitchen with two cups of tea in his hands. He sees the look of alarm on Humphrey's face as our four-legged friend careers down the stairs like a child on the helter-skelter. Rob and I look at each other and burst into fits of laughter.

'For heaven's sake put the tea down before we have another accident!' I holler.

Five hours later the boys return looking tanned and relaxed having clearly had a wonderful time.

Humphrey is in his customary, excited, happy dance overdrive and shoots off in search of a suitable welcome home gift for his masters. He returns with a tea-towel and deposits it ceremoniously at their feet, staring up eagerly at them for approval. Maisy seems to know that something is up but is still standing staring at the wall. Lola waltzes in, nose in the air, tail swishing, before rubbing herself up against James' legs.

'Hello you lot, well this is a lovely welcome home. I can see that you've been well looked after in our absence. I hope you've been behaving yourselves,' he says bending down and giving Humphrey an affectionate hug.

'And what about you two?' asks James. 'I hope you've had a good stay, nothing too eventful I hope?'

Rob gives me a sideways glance. I glare fixedly at his bandaged hand which he surreptitiously slides behind his back.

'No, we've had a wonderful time thanks. They've all been absolute angels!'

# 3

# A BIT OF A CATASTROPHE

"Henri is a bit of a character," reads the sitter's manual. No, he's not an animal. Henri is the cleaner. "He comes on Friday mornings for a couple of hours but you can cancel him if you want." Of course I don't want. My curiosity has been raised and I now want to meet Henri. I realise that my mental image of him has been coloured by my having known someone of the same name when I was still at work, so in my mind he's either small, balding and bespectacled or will arrive on a bicycle with a string of onions round his neck and wearing a striped t-shirt. Time will tell.

Stanley, on the other hand, is a dog and we know what he looks like because we've seen his photograph. In fact it was his photo that made us both go, 'Aaaah!' and apply for the sit. He lives with Smudge who is a cat. Stanley is an elderly West Highland Terrier. The fact that he's reportedly deaf, almost blind and has just had nine teeth removed just makes us go 'Aaaah!' all over again. So, flights booked, we await our escape from the island.

I made a point of explaining to the owners when we arranged to do the sit, that we'd plan to leave home in good time in case of any problems with travel. Forty-six days on our island were affected by fog last year and it looks as though today is no exception as all air travel to and from the mainland has been cancelled. Flights to a winter sit can obviously be grounded by snow with the present weather patterns or, in the case of ferries, cancelled due to rough seas. However, when I explain our thinking to David, the owner, he clearly feels that I'm being over-anxious.

'Don't worry,' he says reassuringly. 'This is the south-east, we never get snow.'

It's during the few days leading up to our imminent departure for Kent that the severe weather warnings are announced. Heavy snowfall is forecast for the UK and is likely to arrive at the exact moment that we should be travelling. Bags packed, ready for our early morning pick-up, it soon becomes apparent that we aren't going anywhere for a while. Although our island snow has turned to rain, Europe is in the grips of a Red Weather Alert and, it seems, the UK is at a stand-still. Fortunately we've already been in touch with the owners and discussed plans B, C and D.

'So what's going to happen if we get there and they still haven't been able to leave?' asks Rob. 'I mean it's going to feel a bit tense moving in with a family that we've never met.'

'Well Ann actually seemed very laid back about it when I talked to her the other day. She just said we could muck in, it didn't seem to bother her at all,' I reply. 'I'm sure we'd cope.'

It's another two days before transport links start working again. David and Ann (about whom we know very little) have had to make an early start so we're to arrive at the house and let ourselves in. We land at Stansted, pick up our hire car and drive gingerly on dirty, thawing snow to our new home, a handsome, detached property on the outskirts of Tunbridge Wells.

'You know Chris, I love the trust that's involved in such situations. I mean these generous people, who've never clapped eyes on us, tell us where to find the key to their house and have faith that we're not going to burgle the place and make off with the contents.'

However, when we arrive, turn the key in the lock and step inside, it looks as though maybe the burglars have got there before us.

The phrase in the Housesitters' Handbook that reads, "We

are not quite as organised as we would like to be," now makes absolute sense. It's clearly housesitter speak for "We live in total chaos". Having dropped our bags in the hallway we look around in astonishment. The floor is carpeted with junk mail and there are all manner of books piled up against the walls lining the corridor, stacked twenty deep. The place is akin to a charity shop that's run out of space to put anything. We wander around the numerous rooms, mouths agape. This is clearly a home that is lived in. Books, musical instruments, lego models, toys, woodwork projects, engineering projects, and a telescope that looks as though it should be at Jodrell Bank, all tell us that this is a family who put life's pleasures before housework. A fridge magnet reads, "The house was clean last week, sorry you missed it!" and on the pantry door a sign states apologetically, "Excuse the mess but we live here." How I'd love to have the courage to subscribe to that. I'm always far too concerned about how others will perceive me if our place is a mess or, even worse, dirty. So Ann and David's home is a welcome relief. No worries about dog or cat hairs on the sofa or the odd crumb on the kitchen table. I'm convinced we'll be happy here.

It suddenly occurs to us that there's no sign of any animals. Maybe they were stolen when the burglars broke in? But no, there in the corner, tucked in its basket is a large white mound, greying at the edges and heaving gently. It's Stanley, (if his photo is anything to go by) and he's snoring. He clearly hasn't heard us arrive. We just have to hope that when he does wake up and finds a couple of strangers in his house that he isn't going to go into attack mode and sink his gums into our ankles.

Suddenly there's a loud, 'Wow'. It's Smudge, a black and white tornado, who has shot through the cat-flap having picked up on the fact that there's activity in the house. The black smudge on his nose is clearly how he got his name, but it makes him look as though he's been nosing in a coal-scuttle.

'Wow', he says again.

And again. And again. In fact the wowing carries on incessantly. He's clearly trying to communicate something but we're not quite sure what at this stage. Knowing cats, we decide it's probably food-related, but not yet having settled in and established where his food is kept we're going to have to keep him waiting. Rob flops down on the settee, tired after our journey. I eventually manage to find the Whiskas and, within seconds, Smudge has wolfed down his food, laid claim to Rob's lap and curled up for a sleep. Minutes later Rob has joined him. I leave them to it and head off to explore the house.

I always feel somewhat awkward wandering around someone else's home, never mind a stranger's, but I reassure myself that we do need to know the extent of our duties and familiarising oneself with the lay-out of the property is essential. A quick shufti and I've got the picture. David obviously operates from the study which is dominated by a large desk akin to the type you'd expect to find in a solicitor's office. However, there is little of the desk on show due to the huge piles of papers, some leaning precariously, that adorn the surface.

A pair of old, etched, glass doors lead through to a very dilapidated conservatory which is crammed full of cacti of every shape and size, some displaying glorious, technicolour flowers. There are prickly ones and hairy ones, short, fat ones and tall, wonky ones. I can't resist the temptation to stroke a couple of them. I've never seen so many varieties in one place. A large sign that has been placed strategically at the front of the display reads, in capital letters, DO NOT WATER. I notice that they all have plant labels, all carefully written on in pencil, each one recording the latin name of its occupant. One particular plant seems at odds with the collection and looks more akin to a scree or rockery plant. It's very low-growing and a strange combination of brown and white but does look decidedly prickly. I reach out to touch it and am surprised by the strange, but decidedly sharp, plastic quality of the leaves. Curious to know what this strange plant is, I carefully remove the wooden label and read 'Hedgeous Hogious Spiniculatum'. It's then that the penny drops and I recoil hastily, realising that I've been tricked by David's apparently wry sense of humour. I trust that there aren't any more creatures masquerading as plants in his collection and head off to investigate the rest of the house.

The two children have the luxury of a play-room, complete with a wide-screen TV, but the floor and furniture are absolutely littered with all manner of toys that appear to have been abandoned. A large wicker hamper in the corner of the room is chock-a block with clothes and shoes and a rather sad-looking, balding, teddy peers out from beneath the jumble. There are dolls and cars, construction toys, lego models galore and an assortment of basketballs, some of them signed. There's even a basketball hoop attached to the wall. My clumsy effort at attempting to score a goal reminds me why I was never chosen to play for the school netball team.

I move on through three bedrooms, two bathrooms, (one pink, one avocado), then wander back to the study to browse at the book-shelves as I always think that someone's reading-matter is one of the best ways of getting to know them. This library suggests an in-depth knowledge of heart engineering, astro-physics, astrology, Buddhism, Russian history and succulents and seems to contain every best-selling novel that's been written in the last forty years. This is better than being in a good book shop. I decide we're going to like it here.

The Housesitters' Handbook also outlines the feeding requirements of both our charges and, on checking the book of words, we learn that Smudge has a heart murmur for which he should be receiving medication. Those of you who have ever lived with a cat (you will appreciate why I avoid using the word 'owned' in this context) will know how notoriously difficult it is to administer tablets to an animal that has sharp claws, teeth and an aggressive streak that can be triggered in seconds if presented with anything even mildly threatening. It's both a foolish and dangerous exercise and one to be avoided at all costs. All those stories about tablets ending up behind the fridge with the cat on top of the curtain pole are not only true but understated. I recall using up an entire blister-pack of hugely over-priced beta-blockers, dispensed by our vet, in one session and then having to retrieve the cat from the top of the next-door neighbours' shed. Dogs, on the other hand are putty in one's hands as all that is required is a piece of cheese, a morsel of sausage or, even better, prosciutto.

Fortunately for us David and Ann have decided not to attempt to medicate Smudge. They kindly reassured us by email before leaving that, should Smudge happen to leave this world during their absence they'd be totally accepting of the fact. In fact both animals had reached that point in their lives when they could be taken any day. As a new carer I'm left feeling more than a little anxious. No pressure then!

There's still snow on the ground although the thaw has begun. Dear old Stanley, having just woken up, has a good sniff of his new guardians but seems quite relaxed and is clearly up for a walk. Rob finds his lead and we head off to explore our new surroundings. We're amazed by how well Stanley manages for an old-timer. He trots along happily showing interest in everything around him, dutifully pees at every gate and lamppost, disappears under bushes and into hedges until we decide it would be wise to turn round before he gets too tired. He steers us both comfortably round what is clearly his customary route then heads for home. First walk done and dusted, our charges fed. All's well with the world.

'D'you know Rob this whole house-sitting thing is really helping me to focus on what matters in life,' I reflect over a much-needed glass of wine later that evening. 'I really prefer houses that are truly homes, not the sort of places where you're constantly fretting about putting your coffee cup down on the furniture or having to take your shoes off before you walk on the carpet. As this lot rightly say, 'We live here'. It's good to be comfy and relaxed and not have to worry about keeping everything just so. Do you remember that time we stayed with Felicity and Michael? Their place was more like being in a show-house.'

'Oh crikey, yes!' replies Rob. 'I remember going to bed and worrying about whether or not I'd put the soap back on that little magnetic thingy that suspended it above the bathroom sink!' he laughs.

'Basin darling, not sink,' I remind him. 'I remember thinking that the evening meal had been delivered to the back door by a team of caterers. How does anyone entertain eight people and leave no sign of anything having been prepared in the kitchen? It was immaculate when I offered to take the glasses through for her. She'd even laundered the table-cloth and serviettes by the time we sat down for breakfast the next day.'

'Napkins,' says Rob. 'I think you mean napkins my love, not serviettes.'

The next day is Sunday so, not having had much of a chance to do any shopping, we have a rather meagre selection of food in the fridge. Just as I'm rooting around wondering what we can have for lunch, there's a loud banging from the utility room which I recognise as the cat-flap. The racket is followed by the most vociferous meow that I ever recall hearing from a cat. One of the cats I had as a child used to love to announce her return with a similar noise, usually when she'd brought us a dead mouse or, even worse, a live one. If I ignored her cries she would then start to fling the poor creature against the panel of the door until blood from her trophy was trickling down the glass.

As Smudge's yowling is getting even louder I suggest to Rob that he goes to investigate as I'm half-way through making us a sandwich. On entering the utility room I hear him cry out,

'Oh my God!'

'Is everything okay?' I shout.

'No!'

'Why, what's the matter?' I holler.

'He's got a chicken!'

'A chicken? Where on earth has he got a chicken from? Is it hurt?'

'Worse than that, it's dead,' is the reply.

'Dead! Oh my God, the poor thing!'

At this point I dash into the utility room to witness the carnage. Rob is standing with a chicken in his hands. A freshly-roasted chicken that's still dripping with warm fat.

'Oh no!' I cry. 'Wherever has he managed to find that?'

'At a guess I should think it was destined to be someone's Sunday lunch,' Rob chuckles.

'But it's no laughing matter Rob. The poor folk must be wondering where on earth it's disappeared to. What do you think we should do?'

'Feed it to Stanley and Smudge?' suggests my ever-helpful man.

'But someone's going to go hungry,' I wail.

'Well, we can hardly go knocking on people's doors with a lukewarm chicken in our hands asking if by any chance it belongs to them, now can we?'

'I suppose not. I guess these two are in for a feast.'

At this point Smudge, who's now looking decidedly aggrieved, slaloms past my feet and disappears through the cat-flap, clearly disgruntled that we've confiscated his trophy. It's about twenty minutes later, just as we're sitting down to lunch, when the characteristic meow echoes yet again from the utility room.

'Oh no. Not again. Let me guess, it's a leg of lamb this time,' I sigh, putting my head in my hands.

Rob sways back on his chair, leaning precariously so that he can see into the utility room.

'Nope,' he replies. 'It's a piece of corned beef.'

'Oh grief, they were probably going to have that after the chicken went missing!' I splutter.

Even I have to admit that it's all becoming a bit of a farce. However, we take the precaution of closing the cat-flap for the rest of the day just in case Smudge decides to help himself to another delicacy. As we sit chomping our cheese sandwiches, we look down enviously at our charges who are tucking into their bowls of warm, diced chicken.

We spend the majority of our time curled up in the snug with the animals, a cosy corner of the house with a TV. In fact we haven't really strayed from this part of the house all week apart from going to bed or using the bathroom. It makes us reflect on the fact that the majority of rooms in the big houses that we've had the privilege of staying in don't get used at all, a bit like the Victorian parlour that was always kept for special occasions.

'I know we get to stay in some pretty special places and then wish we had more space at home, but in reality we actually only occupy four rooms,' muses Rob.

He's right. Big spaces might look wonderful but then they need heating and cleaning and decorating. I've had enough of housework to make me want to avoid increasing the work-load.

'I think I'll take Stan for a walk round the block,' announces Rob. 'Walkies,' he shouts, but dear old Stan is sound asleep and doesn't hear him.

Rob gives him a gentle nudge and a pair of sad eyes look slowly up at him. A tail begins to wag and gradually Stan hauls himself up.

'Come on old fella, let's go for a walk.'

'I'll hang on here and prepare dinner for this evening, then I'll only have to heat it up later,' I suggest.

'Sounds good to me,' replies Rob and disappears through the back door with Stanley.

It's about twenty minutes later when they return, Rob looking unaccustomedly flushed.

'Is everything okay?' I ask. 'You look a bit red in the face.'

'Gosh, that was so embarrassing!' he chokes.

'What was love? What's the old fella done?'

'It's not Stan, it's Smudge again. We were just turning the corner to go down to the green when we literally bumped into this rather posh-looking lady. She wasn't at all pleased but then she looked me straight in the eye, poked me in the chest and said, "Your cat ate our gerbil!" I was so taken aback that I didn't even try to explain that Smudge wasn't my cat.'

'So what did you say?' I ask, choking quietly on a crisp.

'I just apologised. What else could I do? I could hardly deny it now, could I?'

'It was probably her chicken that he nicked too. Ha! Let's hope he doesn't help himself to anything else while we're here,' I snigger.


By Thursday we're feeling quite at home and have settled into a routine with the animals. Stan is happy with a short walk each morning and spends most of his day sleeping. Smudge seems happy providing we fill his food bowl on demand and provide him with a warm lap to sleep on, and so we batten down the hatches and wait excitedly for the cleaner to arrive.

Henri is supposed to arrive at 10 o'clock but it's nearer to eleven when he turns up, earphones plugged in, presumably listening to music. He isn't sporting a striped t-shirt, nor is he wearing spectacles, in fact he looks quite grubby for a cleaner. I greet him at the door and he mumbles a few indecipherable words in return. I detect a foreign accent but he hasn't really said enough for me to work out where he's from. After dumping his leather jacket on the hall floor he disappears, presumably to start work, leaving the air filled with the strong reek of cigarettes.

Much as I have come to like the 'chaos', I do begin to wonder how anyone can begin to clean this place. There's no surface that isn't covered with an assortment of clutter. The spare room is by far the greatest challenge. It seems that the family have been opening the door occasionally for years, throwing an item in there and quickly closing the door before the mountain of clutter creates an avalanche. There are suitcases, boxes and carrier bags all stuffed to the gills with discarded items and all manner of coats, shoes and boots that don't appear to have been worn for years. No-one could make sense of this, no matter how hard they tried. I certainly can't imagine how Henri is going to effect any change.

It's after he's been busy for about an hour that his phone rings. I can't help but eavesdrop as he's in the hallway just outside the kitchen.

'Hello? Oh, hello Boss! I am thinking you are on 'oliday'.

A distant voice can be heard responding, clearly to Henri's surprise.

'Where am I Boss? Why, I iz at home. Yes, I am thinking today is 'oliday.'

Lies I think. All lies. Come on Henri, get yourself out of this one.

'No, no Boss. I no working today. I in bed. I am thinking I 'av 'oliday.'

Curiouser and curiouser.

'Okay Boss, yes I am understanding. You have very nice day Boss. Yes, I work tomorrow no problem. Bye Boss. Bye. Bye.'

Making a bit on the side? Definitely a bit of a character methinks.

It's only when Henri has sloped off following his two hour stint that I go for a wander round. Surprisingly everything does look cleaner. And tidier. And then I see the play-room. Only Mary Poppins could have achieved such a transformation. Miraculously all the toys and clothes are in absolute order and the room looks more like a toy-shop awaiting its first customers.

The whole room is orderly, clean and unrecognisable. I have a new-found respect for Henri. A bit of a character yes but a worker of miracles too!

# 4

# THE ITALIAN JOB

"LUCY STAYS EITHER IN the house or the garden. We never let him out otherwise he disappears." We're somewhat bemused when we read the instructions. How does anyone manage to keep a cat within the confines of a garden? Knowing their ability to scale fences, trees and curtains we could only imagine a high mesh fence with barbed wire and an electric shock system running through it. And how come Lucy is a he? Maybe it was a typo? Anyhow, one cat seems a rather cosy sit. No late night dog-walking or having-to-go-out-in-the-rain-even-if-it's-chucking-it-down. What's more, this sit is in our favourite country, Italy. The penny (or should that be the euro?) drops! Maybe Lucy is short for Luciano?

We'd been applying for house-sits in Italy for a while but so had the rest of the world. The five-week stint in Venice would have been a dream but sadly it was not to be. We were therefore thrilled to get an enthusiastic response from a young Canadian couple living in Treviso saying that they'd love us to look after their cat while they went away for a few days to attend a friend's wedding. So, after exchanging a few emails to firm up the arrangements, we book our flights to Venice and head in-land where we're to be picked up at the railway station by the owners.

Except they don't turn up. Instead, a last-minute text explains that the husband is unexpectedly having to work a late shift at work and requires the car. As he's now unable to collect us could we get the bus instead? If we get on the number 11 outside the station then change to the number 17 at the Leisure Centre and get off at Via Settembre XI we'll be fairly near the house. The fact that it's getting dark and we have no knowledge of the area is making what is supposed to be a simple journey an expedition into the unknown. We decide to play safe and get a taxi. The driver couldn't be more helpful and kindly drops us right outside number 28 Via Dolomiti, €18 poorer. Just as we realise that it's impossible to open the heavy, metal garden gate from the outside a young woman comes out of the front door. Relief! I smile and shout,

'Debbie! Hi!'

The woman looks at me with a puzzled expression.

'Debbie?' I repeat quizzically.

'No, non sono Debbie,' she replies.

'Ma questa è Via Dolomiti numero 28?' I ask having to suddenly tweak my brain into Italian mode.

'No. Via Dolomiti 28 è dietro l'angolo, attraverso i cancelli, dovrá suonare il campanello.'

So the house that we're after, which, curiously, has the same address as the one we're standing outside, is in fact round the corner behind a set of high security gates. Having found the entrance we notice an array of electronic doorbells, some fifty or more, all with the names of the occupants written in microscopic print. It's beginning to get dark and Rob's temper is beginning to fray after a rather long and frustrating day.

'This is ridiculous Chris. How are we supposed to read these damn labels in the dark?'

'Haven't you brought your torch? You usually carry one,' I reply.

'Yes, I have but it's right at the bottom of my suitcase. You know how difficult it was to pack yesterday. If I get everything out I'll probably not be able to get it back in,' he moans.

'Well I don't think we have any choice love. As you say, the labels are impossible to read in this light.'

And so a decidedly weary Rob unzips his case and begins unpacking his neatly-folded clothes and laying them on top of my bag.

'This is the last straw Chris. You know how carefully I put everything in my case. Now look at it.'

'Hang on a minute. I've just realised, I can use the light on my phone.'

'Now you tell me!' says Rob exasperatedly as he starts trying to get his things back in his bag.

While he's cussing under his breath I attempt to read the names beside the bells.

'I hate to say it Rob but I can't see their name anywhere yet we must be in the right place. I'll just have to phone Debbie.'

I do a search and call the number that I've entered into the memory. Except I get a message in Italian that tells me that the number that I'm calling isn't recognised. This is beginning to get complicated. And worrisome.

'Put the international dialling code in Chris, that's why you're not getting through,' suggests Rob helpfully.

I try again and phew! A woman's voice answers and yes, at last, Debbie is coming to find us.

The house is what we would call a starter-home, mid-terrace but within a tastefully-planted, gated community. It's clean, functional and comfortable enough. So, perched on the sofa, still in our coats, we're introduced to Lucy. And yes, surprisingly Lucy is a he, but his name isn't short for Luciano, it's short for Lucifer, and now we understand why. Lucy is velvet black with penetrating, green eyes and is undoubtedly the fattest cat we have ever clapped eyes on. He glares at us, sitting stock still, inspecting us suspiciously. Now we understand why he can't actually get out of the garden. There's no way that he could heave his enormous bulk over the gate which is a mere 2'6" off the ground.

'The vet says he has to lose some weight, but I find it so hard to say no when he wants food. He's my baby, aren't you Lucy?' coos Debbie. 'We brought him over from Toronto when we moved here, there was no way we could leave him behind.'

At this Lucy rolls over onto his back purring and puts his legs in the air. I'm quietly wondering if he'll be able to get himself upright without assistance.

'He loves having his tummy tickled and playing with his furry mouse, don't you sweetie?' and at this she dangles a severely damaged toy over Lucy's head. Lucy downs it with one swipe of his paw. I'm already feeling nervous about tickling this feline's tummy. However, having made all the right noises about our new ward it's suggested that we sit down to eat. The fact that we've yet to be invited to remove our coats doesn't seem to have occurred to Debbie so I suggest that maybe we could take our cases to our room. However, to our dismay, we discover that the pair of them have all their holiday clothes laid out on our bed. No problem we smile, abandon our bags and coats and head downstairs for dinner.

The following morning, en route to the bathroom, I bump into a fresh-faced, tousle-haired young man in a pair of boxer shorts who, I can only assume, is Debbie's husband. It seems a little odd to be shaking hands with a half-naked, total stranger on the landing. He looks decidedly uncomfortable, mumbles something inaudible, then promptly shuffles back into his bedroom and closes the door.

By ten o'clock there's still no sign of breakfast, or even a cup of tea for that matter. By half-past ten I stop being English and simply ask Debbie if it would be okay to put the kettle on.

'I thought maybe we could all go to the supermarket together and pick up a few things,' she replies, 'and then we can have a drink when we get back. Mark's going to make some brownies for breakfast so it'll give him time to get started while we're out.'

'Made' as opposed to 'bought' sounds good but I'm worried about the time-scale. Another half an hour and I'll be heading for a low blood-sugar and collapsing in a heap on their sitting-room floor. We head off to the supermarket and return to witness Mark putting the raw brownie mixture onto a baking tray. It's some time after eleven o'clock that we eventually sit down to break our fast. The brownies are delicious but there's an alarming absence of coffee. I hint gently that a caffeine fix would be welcome and am staggered to discover that these two don't drink coffee! My system immediately switches into an 'I need caffeine' mode. As soon as they leave I'll be hot-footing it back to the supermarket.

A couple of hours later, having seen Debbie and Mark off, we're sitting enjoying a strong double espresso when I happen to glance out into the garden. Lucy, who is sitting next to the gate, mysteriously, and with the utmost ease, lifts his front leg and, with a casual flick of his paw, opens it. He then, amazingly, manages to squeeze through the resulting gap and disappears from sight.

'Oh my God!' I shout. 'Rob, the cat's escaped. They've only been gone two hours and we've lost the damn cat!'

At this I dash out into the walkway and look frantically up and down. There is no sign of Lucifer. Rob joins me and together we search anxiously in the neighbouring gardens. Suddenly a loud miaow comes from under a nearby hedge. Lucifer! Thank goodness. I get down on my knees and make come hither noises. He hisses at me. When I reach forward with my hand he responds with a swift swipe of his paw, claws outstretched.

'Cheese,' I call urgently to Rob. 'There's some cheese in the door of the fridge.'

Within seconds Rob is back with a packet of mozzarella.

'Here Lucy,' I purr, scattering the shavings onto the ground beneath his nose.

He reaches forward to indulge in my bribe but seems suddenly reluctant.

'Come on Lucy. Nice cheese! Yum!' I coax.

Lucy seems decidedly interested in my offering and yet

doesn't make any advance. It's at this point, on hearing him yowl, that we realise that he's stuck, well and truly stuck. Worryingly his back end is on the other side of a neighbour's wire fence, his bulk now divided between the outer walkway and the inner garden. I put my hand forward in an attempt to grab him by the scruff but am immediately met with a decidedly vicious show of claws and an impressive hissy fit.

'We'll have to go and explain to the owners of the house,' says Rob helpfully.

'You mean I'll have to go and explain,' I reply.

'Well yes, I suppose I do mean that,' he smiles apologetically.

I extract myself from the hedge and try to figure out the Italian for, 'Excuse me but the cat that we are looking after has escaped and got itself stuck in your fence,' and very quickly realise that my very limited vocabulary is not going to lend itself to such an explanation.

'You go,' I instruct Rob.

'Me?' he cries. 'Why me?'

'Because you'll be able to charm the owner. You just need to do a few charades. You'll be fine.'

At this Rob glares at me and reluctantly heads off round the corner to knock on the neighbours' door.

Half an hour later we return to base covered in scratches. Rob has also got a nasty puncture wound in his finger. Not one to suffer in silence he reminds me that a cat bite is a great deal more worrying than a dog bite.

'You do realise that I might get an infection,' he whinges, clutching his wound.

At least Lucifer is now secured within the confines of the garden and basement and, for once, I actually share Rob's concern.

'I hate to say it sweetheart but I do think you should have a tetanus injection. You're right about cat bites, they can be really nasty. The last thing we need is you falling ill while we're here. I think we ought to get you to the surgery.'

'No, really I'll be fine,' replies my patient, bravely trying to muster a smile while cradling his injured hand.

'I do think you should see a doctor darling. When did you last have a tetanus jab?'

'Haven't a clue. Years ago I guess. Why, how long do they last?'

'Mmm, about ten years I think. But if you really can't remember when you last had one you're probably way overdue.'

'But I hate injections,' whimpers Rob. 'Needles make me really nervous, Chris.'

'Injection Rob. No excuses. You'd better get there before they close.'

'You will come with me, won't you?' he asks.

'I would, but I don't think we should risk leaving Lucy outside in case he escapes again. I'd better hang on here and try to get him back into the house. Go on, you'll be fine.'

'But I won't be able to explain to the doctor. What if he can't speak English?'

'They all speak English. If he doesn't then you'll just have to do an impression of a hissing cat and show him your claws. Now go on, shoo, before they close.'

Fortunately we'd noticed the local surgery when we went to the supermarket: a rather depressing building that looked more like a run-down youth club, its waiting-room furnished with grubby-looking plastic chairs that were falling apart. The people that we'd seen waiting inside appeared to be in much the same state as the chairs and could be heard coughing and spluttering through the dirty, glass window.

As Rob sets off reluctantly, I can't help reflecting on the fact that he gets really uptight about germs when he visits the doctor. The idea of touching a door-handle, or a magazine that's been in someone else's hands, really freaks him out so he usually carries a little bottle of hand-sanitiser as a precaution. How he's going to survive this experience I hate to think.

It's more than an hour later when he returns looking decidedly sorry for himself.

'Well?' I ask. 'How did you get on?'

'It was awful. That place is the pits Chris. The doctor might have stopped me getting tetanus but goodness knows what else I've managed to pick up. It was so grubby and there were some pretty scary customers in there. I wouldn't want to meet any of them on a dark night.'

'Well never mind, at least you're back. What about the jab? Was it painful?'

'I looked the other way when he stuck the needle in but I do feel a bit bruised. I'll probably have a stiff arm tomorrow.'

'So did the doctor speak English?'

'Funnily enough he was English so thankfully I didn't have to perform a pantomime.'

'I assume he wasn't a Welsh rugby fanatic?' I laugh.

Back home, when Rob moved to a new medical practice, he was registered with a young, Welsh doctor. His first visit must have been around the time of the Six Nations Cup as, picking up on Rob's soft, Scottish burr, Dr Davies immediately assumed that he must have a fellow rugby fan in his surgery. Wishing to ingratiate himself with his new doctor, Rob had stumbled through a discussion of Scotland's chances against Wales in the next round. The problem from then on was that, not having the slightest interest in rugby, but having convinced Dr Davies that he had, Rob's every follow-up appointment had to be preceded by an in-depth search on-line so as to appear knowledgable about the latest results.

'Fortunately we just had a chat about the Italian health system which, ironically, seems to be in a better state than ours,' replies Rob. 'Anyhow, where's our furry friend?'

'I managed to coax him in with yet more food so he's upstairs asleep on our bed. I still haven't worked out how on earth he managed to open the gate in the first place. When it's firmly closed it ought to be impossible for him to open but we'd better keep a watchful eye in future.'

Five days later we still haven't made any progress with Lucy. He remains distant and cool and all he wants is food. We try to ignore his demands but the more we refuse to pay him attention the more vocal he becomes and even starts clawing at the cupboard door where his food is kept. We attempt to drown his plaintive cries by turning up the volume on the TV but all he does is increase the decibel level of his meowing.

'This is going to drive me nuts,' shouts Rob, trying to make himself heard over the blare of the TV. 'I'm going to stand outside for some peace and quiet,' and, at that, Rob steps out of the door into the garden.

No sooner has he crossed the threshold than Lucy sneaks around the side of the door to join him. Within seconds a panicked Rob returns looking absolutely frantic.

'He's gone! He's done it again. He just opened the gate with one flick of his paw and he's gone!'

My mind goes into a spin. We've lost the cat for the second time and it's now pitch dark outside.

'Oh my God, I don't believe it! Which way did he go?' I cry.

'I don't know, I was so horrified that he'd sloped off I didn't notice.'

I'm already anticipating a one-star review on the owners' feedback.

Half an hour later we're still patrolling the walkway. It's pitch-black but our movements keep triggering the communal security lighting.

'LOOOOSEEE,' we cry.

And again. And again. A couple walk past and, seeing us both down on all fours on the path peering under hedges, clearly think we're mad. Curtains start twitching. I go back to the kitchen to get some more cheese from the fridge and scatter it on the lawned area in front of the house. It's at this point that I discover that our 'grass' is actually astroturf. Weird.

Two hours later and there's still no sign of Lucifer. We're frozen to the marrow and we've lost the cat. Feeling absolutely shattered we decide to call it a day, or rather night, return to the house and close the door. I don't know whether to contact Debbie and Mike and risk ruining their holiday. Rob is sitting on the settee with his head in his bandaged hand, looking wretched.

'Let's sleep on it,' I suggest. 'Another night won't change anything. Maybe Italy has a system similar to home where an alert can go out and we can put signs up round the complex.'

We settle down on the sofa, both clearly worried about the outcome of Lucy's disappearance when suddenly a loud 'MIAOW!' echoes from the garden. Rob leaps up and quickly opens the front door. Sitting on the doormat is a large, furry, black lump out of which a pair of malevolent, green eyes are glowering. Not one to waste an opportunity for food, Lucy marches purposefully into the kitchen, glares at Rob and then hurls himself at the cupboard door. Rob dutifully obeys and quickly decants a generous scoopful of dry food into Lucy's bowl. Having ensured that the gate is well and truly locked he closes the front door and, heaving a sigh of relief, we settle down to watch the television.

'Thank goodness he's come back. I hate to think what we'd have said to Debbie and Mark, Rob.'

It's only a matter of minutes before he suddenly jumps to his feet and walks over to the front door. Next to it, behind a curtain, are three switches.

'I think I've got it Chris!' he declares. 'When I tried to switch on the sitting-room lights the other morning, and the outside lights this evening, I must have tried this switch first by mistake.'

He presses it, opens the curtains and, sure enough, we stand and watch while the gate swings open.

'So where is Lucifer?' I ask in a sudden panic.

'He's just gone down to the basement. Hitler's in his bunker,' replies Rob with a satisfied grin.

# 5

## THIS LITTLE PIGGY...

BERTIE IS SITTING BOLT upright in quiet contemplation on the floor of the farmhouse kitchen, his calm demeanour apparent due to the absolute lack of expression on his face. He neither blinks nor moves his eyes and reminds me of the graceful images one sees of temple dogs. Molly, on the other hand, a rather dishevelled, long-haired Jack Russell, is nestled on the sofa beside an embroidered cushion which reads, 'No dogs on this sofa'.

Bertie is a Wheaten terrier, soft and silky and with a gentle nature to match. He's the sort of dog that you can fall for instantly as he's good-tempered, adoring and obedient. He's already become my Number One Dog. Molly on the other hand is a feisty little lady with a stubborn temperament who, for one so small, manages to control all three of us. She has the rather cute looks of a Yorkshire terrier but her tousled hair gives her a slightly manic look and the eyes that peer out from under the thatch say there's no messing with this dog.

Molly and Bertie live in a four hundred year-old Welsh longhouse, buried at the end of a deep river-valley. The scenery is stunning but this is as remote as it gets. The nearest shop is four miles away down a one-track lane, so being organised on the domestic front is essential. Because of the isolated position of the house security is low on the list, in fact the back door hasn't been locked since the family moved in twenty-seven years ago and they don't have a clue where the key is. I can't help comparing this with a couple of sits where we've had to set burglar alarms before popping down to the local shop. I know which arrangement I prefer.

I'd talked to the owner, Henry Caradoc-Evans, a couple of times on the phone prior to our arrival. A well-spoken man with no trace of a Welsh accent who seemed unable to hold a conversation without constantly interrupting me. He'd let me know almost immediately that his wife was a doctor and that they were heading over to Vienna to attend a christening, taking with them one of their three sons (a lawyer) who was visiting from South Africa.

Henry proves to be a rather attractive man, a little like Lucian Freud and with a similarly seductive nature. I can sense Rob's unease as Henry flirts with me unashamedly. Not having been flirted with for some twenty years or more I rather enjoy the attention.

We're given a brief tour of the house with Molly close at our heels. It's a fascinating building, filled with beautiful antique furniture, paintings and expensive fabrics. Upstairs the undulating, wooden floorboards creak as we're shown to our room, a delightful, airy space with wonderful views into the valley and beyond to the Brecon Beacons. It really is magnificent. The clouds cast moving shadows onto a dramatic escarpment where scraggy sheep graze in the bracken. There are freshly-cut flowers at the bed-side, a couple of towels that have undoubtedly seen better days on the chair, and a decidedly old, iron bed, propped up on chocks of wood at one side to allow for the down-hill slope of the floor. It's quirky but charming.

'The dogs are pretty straightforward,' announces Henry. 'They just need their can of meat in the evening, although Molly'll try and convince you she's starving most of the time. Oh, and I'd better show you the pigs hadn't I?'

Pigs? What pigs? I don't recall seeing any mention of pigs on the web-site and if I had I'd have had second thoughts. I try not to let my expression give away my surprise and, what's more, I wonder how Rob's going to respond as he learns about this unexpected addition to our responsibilities. I look at him apologetically, thrusting my upturned hands in the air, Italian style, while Henry isn't looking, unsure why I feel that the inclusion of two porcine companions is somehow my fault. Maybe I'd read the advert in too great a hurry and failed to notice that they were part of the deal.

'They're no trouble at all,' says Henry as we amble down the lane to a nearby field. 'They just need checking on a couple of times a day and their water topped up. Any problems you can ring Daffyd Thomas, our neighbour, he'd always help out. His number's on the emergency contact sheet that I've left for you.'

'Don't they need feeding?' I ask with surprise.

'No, they eat grass, so no need,' replies Henry. 'You can chuck them the odd apple or any left-over fruit or veg, no potatoes or onions though, but they'll be fine at this time of year. They're a greedy pair.'

I've looked after pigs before, Tamworths and Gloucester Old Spots, but I have never in my life seen any pigs quite as comical-looking as this pair. As we approach their field they pick up on the sound of our voices and two sizeable, but extremely low-slung, pigs emerge from under an oak tree and come hurrying across the field to greet us. I say hurrying but their stomachs are so big that their progress is slowed somewhat by their undercarriages. They look like something out of a Walt Disney cartoon. Their faces seem to have permanent smiles and their tiny eyes, framed by stubby eye-lashes, peer at us in the way that short-sighted humans do when they ought to be wearing their glasses. Their tough skin is coated with really coarse, creamy-coloured hair but in places the bristle becomes a dark chestnut. They look rather like porcine bats and feel like yard-brooms. However, it's their huge, plastic-like noses with flaring nostrils that are so amusing. I recall a friend who grew up with pigs as a child telling me that she could never resist the temptation of sticking her finger up their nostrils. For the first time I understand what she was talking about.

'What sort of pigs are they?' I ask Henry, trying to hide the fact that I'm still in shock following his revelation.

'Kunekune,' he replies, (pronouncing them as Coonycoony). 'They hail originally from New Zealand. Were almost extinct at one point.'

I'm still bewildered. I've never heard of the breed before but these two look really cute and seem good-natured.

'Are you keeping them as pets or are they heading for the freezer?' asks Rob.

I consider this a really tactless remark, especially in front of the poor animals and glower at him, but Henry's unfazed.

'Pets I'm afraid,' he replies. 'Sarah's furious. We bought them thinking that we'd see a good return but the grandkids fell in love with them, so now we can't possibly send them to the slaughter-house.'

'Do they live long?' I ask hesitantly.

'I'm afraid so,' Henry sighs. 'Twenty years on average but they can go on to thirty-five, God help us!'

'So I guess they have names,' surmises Rob.

'I thought you might wonder about that,' says Henry looking slightly embarrassed. 'I'm afraid it's Hamlet and Ophelia. Our granddaughter was studying Hamlet for her GCSEs. Still, I suppose it's better than Sausage and Bacon.'

Rob and I exchange bemused looks. This is going to be fun.

We return to the house where the dogs have sensed that something's up. Molly has climbed into the passenger seat of the rather shabby Volvo estate and is emitting a very throaty, threatening growl as Henry tries to remove her.

'She always does this,' he laughs, grabbing her by the scruff and thrusting her into Rob's arms where she scrabbles to be released.

Clearly keen to get moving, Henry bids us farewell, (a rather fond farewell in my case), climbs into the car, starts the engine and drives off in a cloud of grey dust to collect his wife from her surgery before heading to the airport.

So, this is it. Our home for the next ten days. Wonderful. After several hours taken up by arriving, settling in and bidding our host farewell, I realise that I need to head for the bathroom. However, it does prove somewhat unnerving to be sitting on the loo surrounded by twenty-seven rugby elevens from Christ College. It would seem that 'the boys' (Rupert, Rowley and Hugo) all attended this reputable school, following in their father's footsteps. Upon graduation, Henry had gone on to become a highly successful barrister (okay, I checked him out on google) and it appears that the boys are all doing well in their respective careers. There are numerous, framed photos of them around the house and it's clear that the young men have inherited their father's good looks.

Seduced by the apparent luxury of the rest of the house and its tasteful furnishings, nothing could have prepared me for the kitchen. This is a farmhouse kitchen in every sense of the word, but we're not talking chic 1970s Laura Ashley here, we're talking 1930s James Herriot. The furniture is shabby and worn and decidedly grubby. The cushions are stained and the arms of the chairs worn through to the stuffing. The quintessential pine table is covered with the crumbs of countless meals and the dresser so cluttered that it's difficult to find anything useful. There are umpteen cards from birthdays long past as well as a couple of invitations to weddings and 'dos'. 'Mr and Mrs Hyphen-Hyphen request the pleasure of Henry and Sarah Caradoc-Evans at the wedding of their daughter Annabella.'

I've come to realise that girls' names that end with an 'a' somehow have a certain cadence which is lacking in an otherwise dull name. Hence Annabella is preferable to Annabel, Clarissa more classy than Claire. If only my parents had thought of that. I rather like the idea of being called Christina.

An unusual assortment of mugs is piled up on a shelf that slopes so seriously that you imagine that they're all about to slide onto the floor. Another open shelf holds an assortment of plates, none of which match, and a few chipped bowls, mostly in the blue and white designs that are often seen on the cover of Country Life magazine. The huge, stone, inglenook fireplace, complete with bread-oven, is furnished with the customary Aga and, in a snug niche on the floor, lie Molly and Bertie's beds. All in all a homely, unpretentious feel and more or less organised. But that was before I opened the cupboards.

It's only on going to the sink to wash a couple of dishes that I begin to search for the washing-up liquid. There doesn't appear to be any on the work-top so I assume that it must be under the sink which is where most households seem to keep such items. I open the cupboard with some difficulty. A door immediately collapses onto one hinge and a strong smell of damp exudes from within. To my horror it looks as though someone has thrown an assortment of cleaning agents from yesteryear in there and hasn't touched anything for several months, if not years. The containers are coated in either dirt or grease, and the bottom shelf of the cupboard has warped so much that none of the bottles can stand upright. The result looks more like something from a packaging museum that closed down in the 1950s. Some of this stuff must be collectors' items by now, especially the old, rusted tins of Brasso and Duraglit. I reach in tentatively for the Fairy Liquid, fully expecting to find the odd dead mouse or, even worse, a live one. Fortunately neither materialises. I reach for a bar of soap that has adhered itself to the shelf. It's turned a nasty shade of orange and has a couple of dead flies firmly embedded in one end. It's at this point that Rob, who's sitting at the farmhouse table, suddenly looks up.

'Did I just see a pig heading past the gate?'

'A pig?' I reply. 'I hope not.'

'I hate to say it Chris but I'm sure it was. We'd better go and investigate.'

Putting his brain into gear, Rob grabs the dog's lead from

behind the door and dashes out of the yard. I follow in less than hot pursuit, running not being my forté.

Sure enough, heading off at an extended trot down the lane is one of the Kunekune pigs. I'm impressed by the speed of the beast considering his bulk (or hers as we haven't yet worked out which one it is). Fortunately a large walnut tree has started shedding its first fruit so Mr (or Mrs) Kunekune stops for a snack. The tough, green walnuts are crunched with ease and quickly become an alarming emerald-coloured mush that exudes from the pig's mouth like foam. Rob deftly manages to get the dog's lead round its neck and, with brute force, succeeds in turning our new friend in the direction of home.

When we manage to get the runaway pig back to the field it's clear that a section of fence has been uprooted and an easy escape route established. Fortunately Pig No 2 doesn't seem to have caught on to Pig No 1's brush with freedom, but there's clearly a need for some serious DIY.

I hate to do my husband down as he's good at so many things but, when things need fixing, he tends to reach either for the Blu Tack, Superglue or WD40. While at times these prove most successful, at others they seem to have minimal effect. Unfortunately this job is one that's going to need something a little more substantial, such as a heavy sledge-hammer and a few sturdy, wooden stakes.

We erect a make-shift fence while we go in search of the necessary materials. It's only at this point that we discover that the contents of the barn and adjoining stable are much like the contents of the kitchen cupboard except a great deal more challenging. After climbing over a huge pile of obsolete gym equipment, an old tractor, a couple of discarded kitchen cabinets and several pieces of furniture, all of which are covered with grime and bird droppings, we unearth a couple of rather flimsy, wooden poles but there's no hammer to be seen.

'We'll just have to use this old metal pole as a hammer,'

suggests Rob, hauling what looks vaguely like a scaffolding pole from the debris.

An hour later Hamlet and Ophelia's field is well and truly enclosed through Rob's efforts. A couple of discarded pallets have been firmly attached to the two poles and the fence now looks more like a scene from Colditz, but hopefully it'll prove pig-proof. I head back to the house and a well-earned glass of wine while Rob heads for the shower. Except I can't find a cork-screw and unfortunately this is, unusually, not a screw-top bottle. We bought it as part of a deal in the duty-free shop on the ferry and, to my dismay, it comes with a cork. After twenty minutes of scouring the kitchen I'm beginning to consider driving the eight miles necessary to purchase another bottle. I seriously need wine. I picture the cartoon that hangs on the kitchen wall at home depicting a desperate woman holding the neck of a bottle over a railway line awaiting the next passing train. Sadly we are miles away from a rail network.

Bertie is giving me 'The Stare'. Molly, on the other hand, is careering around the kitchen barking furiously. I can't work out what this is all about then suddenly realise that the piggy drama has proved such a distraction that we've forgotten to feed the dogs. I head into the boot-room (posh word for the utility-room cum pantry) and lift a tin down from the shelf. Bertie is clearly excited by now and Mollie positively hyper. Her bark turns into an excited, high-pitched yap at a decibel level that is on the brink of causing pain. I get their bowls ready and reach for the tin.

Now normally tins of dog food come with a ring-pull top and are therefore easily opened. Not this one. So now the hunt for a tin-opener begins. After ten unfruitful minutes of searching in various drawers I'm ready to drive a screwdriver through the lid as both dogs are now both hungry, frustrated and close to attack mode. Bertie has joined Mollie in vocal protest and Rob has reappeared to find out what's going on.

'Problem?' he asks.

I resist swearing at him.

'I can't find a tin-opener,' I shout. 'Or a cork-screw.'

Instead of starting to search the dresser or open a few drawers he walks off in the opposite direction and my fury rises, as does the level of barking. My man can be so infuriating at times. Two minutes later he returns with a big smile on his face.

'Is this what you were looking for?'

He holds out his hands. In one is a tin-opener, in the other a corkscrew. I love this man to pieces.

'You star! You absolute star! Where did you find them?' I ask.

'In the car. I brought them with us after the last time this happened.'

I grab the bottle of wine and thrust it in his hand then head for the boot room with the tin-opener. All is well with the world.

# 6

# ONE FOR SORROW

"Sophie likes her toast buttered," read the instructions that Jennifer and Paul have left for us in the kitchen. You've got it, Sophie is a dog. A young, gentle labradoodle who simply loves company. She eats well but recent, undiagnosed medical problems allow for a little indulgence and the occasional piece of buttered toast seems the ideal comfort. She sits obediently and takes the treat oh so gently from my hand. Labradoodles have the huge advantage of not being hairy and Sophie's soft, golden-brown fur is short and silky, resulting in her looking rather like a large, doleful, teddy bear. She smells strongly of lavender thanks to a doggy embrocation which needs massaging into her legs to ease the discomfort in her back end. Although she's being treated with pain-killers she struggles to walk far, so our exercise tends to be restricted to gentle ambles around the garden. It all seems rather sad for such a young dog.

'Poor lass, she's clearly still in pain, Chris. It's so sad to see such a youngster unable to enjoy life. I hope they manage to sort her out at the vet's. Is it a breed that's prone to this sort of thing?'

'Jennifer said that they think it's most likely hip dysplasia which is quite a common complaint in labs and I think it can lead to arthritis. But as you say, it's sad to see such a young dog suffering like this. It's no fun for her bless her.'

The house, which sits in the depths of the Dorset countryside, is stunning and surrounded by the most beautiful landscaped gardens, complete with stream, and with the added luxury of several acres of private woodland. It's an old, flint farmhouse with original, wooden, sash windows, a huge porch and an old-fashioned conservatory, the traditional sort, which is furnished with all manner of exotic plants. There's a wonderful earthy smell and a fitting humidity that helps the plants to flourish. As a keen gardener, I have to try hard to curb my envy.

Caring for Sophie is a totally different business to our previous sits. Within two days we've become almost as sedentary as she is and spend most of our time curled up in one or the other of the copious armchairs with a good book. She lies on her duvet, occasionally heaves herself up, turns round and plonks herself down again with a weary sigh. From time to time she makes a pleasant grumbling noise while she sleeps which occasionally erupts into a gentle snore.

Although Sophie's owners, a lovely, elderly couple, are understandably concerned about her coping in their absence, she seems very contented. Driving off and leaving her behind had clearly been an emotional moment for them both, but their baby seems decidedly relaxed in our company. Sadly their journey is in order for them to attend the funeral of a close friend who has died following a protracted illness. It was clearly a difficult time, but we were able to reassure them that Sophie would be happier in the familiar surroundings of her own home than fretting in a boarding kennel.

We keep to her routine and, having bodily heaved her to her feet, accompany her on a slow amble around the garden. We make a tour of a magnificent magnolia and the extensive shrubbery before lumbering back through the front door to the sitting-room. She likes to lie close to me which I love. It also gets me even with Rob on the points system, he having taken the lead in the popularity stakes after the last sit. I reckon Sophie's a ladies' dog. She enjoys her massage, especially around her poor back legs. In the evening I sit on the floor with my back against the settee rubbing lavender oil gently into her curly coat while she lies happily beside me with her head on my lap. Bliss!

The sitting-room is a really cosy part of the house, filled

with beautiful ornaments and paintings. The top of the writing-bureau is covered with a range of framed photographs of people that I presume to be Jennifer and Paul's children and grand-children. There are also a couple of pictures of Sophie and in one she's curled up with a very handsome ginger cat.

'Rob, have you seen this?' I ask showing him the photo. 'I reckon they must have had a cat at some point as well as Sophie. He's a handsome fellow isn't he?'

'Mmm. They look like good buddies don't they? I'm always surprised how many dogs seem to get on with cats. Not like our old boy, he'd have torn any cat he clapped eyes on to shreds given half a chance.'

'I guess the cat must have died but they've never mentioned him. How sad.'

Having drawn the short straw with cleaning up the kitchen after dinner, I return to the sitting-room later to find Rob on all fours talking to Sophie who is lying on her duvet. He's clearly trying to win her affections but I reckon it's too late. She's definitely my dog. Seeing Rob's backside waving in the air sets me off into a fit of giggles.

'What's so funny?' he asks, spinning round and glaring at me.

'Seeing your bum in the air. It just reminded me of that time we stayed in that hotel in Italy!' I chuckle. 'You remember, that time when I caught you talking to that half-naked woman?'

'You're never going to let me forget that are you?' moans Rob.

It was a couple of years back when we'd decided to drive down to Italy in our dear old camper van, taking our own dog, Holly, with us. We were suitably impressed that the vast majority of Italian hotels were very relaxed about accommodating a dog, often at no extra charge, and had been able to book a room for the three of us without any problem. One day, on returning to our room, I was greeted by Rob's backside waving in the air, he being deep in conversation with a rather glamorous, Italian woman whose room adjoined ours. The lady was also on all fours, talking to Rob through the gap below the canopy that divided her balcony from ours. She was clinging on to a small Maltese terrier that seemed to be the focus of their conversation. I hovered in the background until the conversation ended and Rob reversed into our bedroom with a rather large grin on his face.

'Oh, hello darling! I've just been talking to the woman in the next room,' he announced. 'Her dog had managed to get under the canopy and come into our room so we were just having a chat. She's called Mimi, she's a Maltese terrier.'

'Yes, I had noticed,' I replied. 'And I also noticed that your new lady-friend was stark naked from the waist down.'

At this point Rob's jaw dropped, his mouth hung open and his face flushed.

'Naked?' he gasped. 'You mean she was knickerless?'

'Absolutely darling,' I replied, arms folded across my chest.

'Oh good grief, I never even noticed!'

'Of course you didn't, I'm sure you were far too interested in Mimi.'

(I'd actually found the whole event amusing but couldn't resist winding Rob up from then on whenever there was an opportunity.)

The bird life in the grounds of our new home is extraordinary and we manage to while away hours watching the many visitors to the bird-feeding station. Throughout the day it's possible to witness at least half a dozen species flying in to feed. There are regular visits from nuthatches, tree-creepers, goldfinches, willow-tits and bullfinches. Occasionally two woodpeckers appear and vie for the mealy-worms in one of the feeders or sit on a nearby, rotting post and drill noisily for insects. A pair of blackbirds are clearly nesting in the hedge, the parents obviously awaiting the arrival of their brood. The stream attracts a dipper and even the occasional heron, a handsome bird that seems to be unperturbed by our presence. It's a veritable bird-watcher's paradise. Unfortunately we also suffer magpies, nasty, aggressive creatures who frequently fly into the midst of the feathered assembly and frighten away our welcome visitors.

It's one morning while we're sitting relaxing in the garden, Sophie dozing dutifully by my feet, that we notice that the blackbirds seem to be unaccustomedly restless.

'They don't seem very happy this morning, do they?' observes Rob. 'Something's obviously upsetting them. They've been making their alarm cry for the past few minutes yet I can't work out what's troubling them. Maybe there's a cat around?'

It's only then that we realise the cause of their upset. It appears that the marauding magpies are planning an assault. The beastly creatures have worked out that there are eggs available for the stealing and are intent on frightening the parents away in order to seize their loot. We run around, noisily clapping our hands and waving our arms in the air in order to frighten them away, but they're not deterred and we realise that, without a twenty-four hour watch, our efforts are totally useless.

Later that day, returning to a sunny spot in the garden for a civilised cup of afternoon tea, Rob suddenly notices one of the magpies hopping determinedly towards the open front door of the porch. The next moment the varmint has entered the house and disappeared from sight.

'Oh no Chris! I hate to say this but one of the magpies has just gone into the house,' he cries.

I jump to my feet, immediately having visions of bird-droppings throughout the hallway, but realise that, if we go in search of the bird with the intention of capturing it, there's going to be a rather nasty mess all over the hall carpet.

'We'll have to try to catch it,' says Rob. 'We can't possibly leave it to fly around in there, it'll create merry hell.'

Now when Rob says 'we' what he really means is 'you' as

he's terrified of handling birds. I can't pretend to be too keen either, but have managed in the past to handle chickens, a blue-tit and a black-backed gull, the latter being a particularly huge and savage creature with a beak like a dagger. So, grabbing one of the doggy towels from the porch, we creep in through the front door. There's no sign of the bird. Nor, fortunately, is there any evidence of it having made a mess in the hall. So far so good. But where is the damn creature? We tiptoe carefully up the stairs until we detect a noise coming from one of the bedrooms. The white room. The wretched bird has managed to fly into the one room in the house that is furnished purely in white. Except it doesn't look very pure any more. This character must have been gorging on berries and the evidence is all over the bedspread, the carpet and the window-sill.

By now the magpie is flapping frantically against the window and it's only on being in such close proximity that we realise just how big these brutes are. This fellow is a king-sized beast and his beak looks decidedly menacing. I hold the towel bull-fighter style, walk slowly towards the window and, with the determined action of someone putting out a fire in a chip-pan, fling the towel over the flapping bird. To my relief our intruder becomes instantly quiet, so I quickly move forward and grab the bundle while Rob manages to open the catch on the sash window. I let go of the murderous creature and, his freedom gained, we watch him fly defiantly back to the bird feeders.

Two hours later the bedding is hanging on the line, all stains removed, thanks to a large dose of Vanish, and I'm carefully removing the stained tufts from the carpet with a pair of nail-scissors. The front door is firmly shut, Sophie is dozing in her bed and all is calm.

'So do we tell them?' I ask Rob.

'Tell who what?'

'Do we let Jennifer and Paul know about the magpie?'

We wrestle with our consciences. 'One for sorrow.' A bird

in the house in this part of the country is considered an ill-omen, never mind it being a solitary magpie. That's where the difficulty lies. If this couple are superstitious then our story could really distress them. Even we've been left feeling unsettled by the experience, despite the fact that neither of us attaches much importance to folklore. On reflection we decide that, as there was no major damage done and there are no tell-tale signs of the invasion, we'll just keep quiet.

It's only a few weeks later, having returned home, that an email arrives from Jennifer. I gasp audibly.

'Something wrong?' asks Rob.

I hand him my ipad unable to read the message aloud.

*'Sad news I'm afraid but we thought you'd want to know. We had to say goodbye to dear Sophie yesterday. We realised that the time had come. Further tests last week resulted in the vet finding a tumour on her spine. The prognosis wasn't good and she was really struggling. We realised that we were hanging onto her for our sakes which was unfair. Needless to say we're in pieces and shall miss her horribly. We just wanted to say thank you so much for all that you did for her.*
*Our love to you both,*
*Jenny x'*

# 7

# CZECH MATES

'Oh, that's a pity,' I sigh.

'What's that love?' enquires Rob.

'We didn't get that sit that I'd applied for, you know, the one with the two cats and the Husky?'

'Oh, that's a shame, he looked a handsome fellow. But I've forgotten, where did you say that one was?'

'Tromso,' I mumble. (I hadn't actually confessed this to Rob when I applied).

'Tromso? Where on earth's Tromso? It sounds like a remote Scottish island.'

'Mmm. No, it's a bit further north than that. It's at the top end of Norway, way up above the Arctic Circle,' I confess, anticipating his response.

'Norway? What on earth were you thinking of Chris? You know I can't stand the cold. When was it for?'

(Rob's voice has gone up several pitches, as predicted).

'January,' I laugh.

'January! But it'd be dark all the time and we'd freeze to death!'

'Yes, I know, but we'd have been able to see the northern lights and the midnight sun. I just felt we ought to start being a bit more adventurous.'

'Chris, there's adventurous and adventurous. We don't need to go on a bloomin' Arctic expedition. Why on earth would we want to go somewhere where we'd be sitting around in the dark for days? You know I get depressed during the winter months. Couldn't you try to find something a bit closer to home and warmer? And in future I'd appreciate it if you were a bit more explicit about the details!'

It's approaching Christmas and the web-site that we use to find housesits is awash with folk all over the world seeking sitters for the holiday period. The trouble is that we're obviously not the only couple seeking an attractive Yuletide get-away. Owners are being inundated by sitters applying for a foreign Christmas so it's a welcome surprise when I receive a reply from a couple in the Czech Republic who are seeking someone to look after their home and dogs while they go to visit family in Germany.

'Rob! We've got it!' I cry excitedly.

'Hang on a minute, so which of the many destinations that you've applied for recently are we heading to?' he asks warily.

'Prague! It'll be beautiful and there'll be Christmas markets and we might even get snow!' I enthuse.

'And dare I ask what we're looking after this time? A Czechoslovakian wolfdog?'

'No, no, it's a sausage dog and a Newfoundland,' I inform him.

'A Newfoundland? Good grief Chris, they're huge animals! Can you imagine how ridiculous that combination's going to look when you take them for a walk? We'll either have to take them out separately or after dark.'

Špagetka (that's Shpagetka) and Sonya prove to be a comical combination but, nevertheless, two lovely characters who are devoted to one another. Spaggy, as we've come to call him, is a long-haired Dachshund with eyes like pools, but this is a sausage-dog on speed! He does everything in top gear and rushes around at such a pace that there's a constant danger of being tripped up. Sonya, by comparison, seems to do everything in slow motion and ambles along, rarely getting out of first gear. Her thick coat is delightfully soft and smells wonderful, a rich earthy smell. I love to give her a hug so that I can bury my head in her fur just to enjoy her scent. She loves to be groomed and readily rolls over onto her back so that I can brush her tummy. She's an absolute darling. A darling that is, apart from the dribble. We'd never realised, until we looked after Sonya, that Newfies have a rather revolting habit of dribbling. A lot. If our dear lady gets excited, especially if there's food around, or if she's overheated, then large strings of drool start to hang from her jowls creating the most unattractive spectacle. If you don't manage to mop it up before it hits the floor then the consequences are even more revolting as she then proceeds to shake her head, resulting in huge quantities of slobber being distributed in all directions, collecting on furnishings, walls, clothing and, even worse, flesh. It's not something you want to experience too often, if at all.

Sonya is, unfortunately, an excessive dribbler. Anticipating food or returning to the house after a walk seem to trigger an abundant flow of slobber from her rubbery jowls. We soon catch on to the triggers so that when either of us sees the onset of drool, the loud cry of, 'Dribble alert!' is enough to send us both leaping out of spraying distance. The mopping-up exercise that is necessitated by one of her slobber attacks is a pretty disgusting affair, involving the use of several tissues and a sponge. We reckon that it must make socialising in someone else's house with her in tow a rather delicate and somewhat embarrassing operation.

In spite of Rob's reluctance to be seen walking Little and Large together, he soon gets over his inhibitions as everyone in the neighbourhood seems to know these two. We're greeted by cheery waves and cries of 'Dobry den!' as the locals bid us good morning when we pass. The children love to come and stroke Sonya and she loves the attention. Little Vaçlav, who lives in one of the neighbouring houses, enjoys nothing more than to be lifted onto her back as if he's astride a huge, furry horse, and to be led down the road holding on to her thick coat. She lollops along like a small pony, her huge tail batting from side to side as she walks.

The owners, Alena and Mirek, had been unable to spend much time with us due to some rather hurried last-minute travel arrangements, but had made us very welcome and also managed a very brief introduction to their next door neighbours, Lubor and Lenka. It seems that Lenka speaks a little English so if we have a problem she should be able to help.

We spend the few days leading up to Christmas exploring the city, enjoying the buskers on Charles Bridge and visiting the Christmas markets. We admire the wonderful puppets and ironmongery adorning the stalls, drink grog to warm us up and gorge on samples of the local meats and cheeses. It's a lovely atmosphere and everyone is cheerful with the imminent approach of the festivities. We're prepared for the fact that, like much of Europe, the climax will be Christmas Eve, unlike at home. Large carp, the traditional Czech Christmas dinner, are for sale in the market, huge creatures that we don't like the look of, neither of us being very keen on fish. I feel rather sorry for them swimming around in big plastic barrels, waiting to be scooped out and taken to their last resting-place before being eaten. I suppose, on reflection, that it's no different to us raising turkeys in their thousands whose destiny is to be stuffed, roasted and carved up, except we don't have to murder our Christmas dinner before we eat it.

Two days before Christmas Eve there's a dramatic dip in the temperature and the sky turns an alarming shade of gunmetal grey.

'Looks as though it's going to snow,' observes Rob.

'Oh brilliant!' I enthuse. 'It'll look so pretty and just in time for Christmas.'

By tea-time large flakes are beginning to fall and at six o'clock the snow is rapidly beginning to form a wonderful, pristine blanket that turns the world outside the house into a Christmas card.

'Oh, Rob, it's beautiful! Come and look,' I gasp.

'Beautiful it might be but we'll need to take these two for their last walk later. Let's hope we don't get much more before bed-time.'

By ten o'clock the snow has piled up against the back door and is already drifting across the driveway. We put the leads on Spaggy and Sonya, don our snow-boots and winter gear and open the door. An icy blast hits us and Spaggy withdraws quickly into the kitchen.

'Come on Spaggy, we've got to go out!' I say encouragingly.

He pulls on the lead and disappears under the kitchen table.

'Well, you can't blame him can you?' says Rob. 'He's going to have a frozen undercarriage if we drag him through this. Here, you take Sonya and I'll try to get him to go in the garden.'

So Sonya and I set off for the evening constitutional. She pads quietly along leaving paw prints the size of a bear's. It seems a shame to spoil the virgin snow but this lady needs to walk round the block before bed-time. I tread carefully as it's already slippery underfoot in places. As we walk round the loop that'll take us back home, we can see in through people's windows and I'm able to admire the Christmas trees and decorations adorning the houses. A foreign, snowy Christmas seems to be the perfect way to spend the festive season.

It's a strange area of fairly new residential housing, much of which still seems to be under construction. Very few of the houses have had the outer skin applied and so are still bare breeze-blocks, although the interiors seem to be fully functional. I assume that a lot of folk are doing a self-build and have simply considered getting into the house their priority and will clad the shell later when they have the time and the money.

I head back in the direction of our new home, Sonya enjoying the snow and occasionally pouncing at the drifts and eating great mouthfuls. The snow sticks to her fur and forms white socks on her legs. It's only as we turn a corner that I notice a large neon sign sticking out from the side of one of the houses and, for a moment, I'm taken by surprise. In large red letters are the words 'SEX SHOP'. It's not just the curious context of this being on a private estate, it's the fact that the shop appears to be in someone's living-room. I hurry back to tell Rob who's as amused and as puzzled as I am.

'I mean it's such a weird place to have one!' I exclaim. 'You can't imagine that sort of thing at home can you? There'd be objections galore submitted to the Planning Department.'

'Maybe we'll have to go and explore before we leave,' suggests Rob, leering at me with a raised eyebrow.

It's the next morning, the day before Christmas Eve, that the temperature inside the house seems to have plummeted dramatically. We've already grown accustomed to the benefits of the under-floor heating but it seems to be suddenly inefficient.

'It must be struggling to warm up the house at the moment,' reasons Rob. 'It's got to be a good few degrees below zero out there.'

By lunchtime we're really feeling the chill settle in the house and decide that there must be a problem. Rob ventures down to the boiler-room and, on returning, announces that the boiler seems to have gone out.

'Oh no!' I moan. 'What a time to have a problem with the heating. I wonder if Lubor and Lenka can help?'

'So what's the Czech for "our central heating seems to have broken down"?' asks Rob.

'Ha ha,' I reply, doubting that Lenka's limited vocabulary is going to stretch to that. 'I'll have to Google it.'

I reach for the laptop and do a quick search on Google Translate.

'It's no good Rob. I haven't a clue how to pronounce it,' I reply, stumbling through the strange assortment of letters.

I always like to attempt to communicate in another language, even if it's only the basics, but this one has me totally confused. How can anyone begin to pronounce words that have no vowels in them? I click on the icon which reads the phrase out aloud and realise immediately that I have absolutely no chance of memorising it.

'I'll have to write it down phonetically for you,' I inform Rob.

'What do you mean, 'for me'? You can go for a change. Anyhow you're better at languages than I am and they're likely to respond more favourably to a damsel in distress.'

And so, with piece of paper in hand, I don my snow-boots and plod next door to see the neighbours.

Lubor comes to the door and welcomes me warmly but, to my horror, he's wearing nothing but a t-shirt and a pair of rather unattractive y-fronts. He's a large man, probably in his late fifties, and it's not a pretty sight. I try to avert my eyes as he invites me into the house. The heat inside hits me, it's toasty warm and I can already feel my fingers thawing.

'Lenka! Lenka! Kristina je zde!' he cries.

Lenka appears at the top of the stairs wearing a fetching, low-topped chiffon blouse and a pair of red knickers. Although she's a great deal more attractive than her husband I'm beginning to feel decidedly awkward. In fact I think I should make a hasty retreat and let them get on with whatever it was they were doing before I called.

I'm now trying to avoid eye-contact with both of them and avert my gaze to the wall in the hall-way, reach into my pocket and hand them my scrawled translation. They read it, look up with anxious faces and mutter a few words to one another. At this point Lubor shuffles upstairs and returns, having, much to my relief, donned a pair of trousers, indicating that he'll come back with me to see if he can help.

Back at base I accompany Lubor to the boiler-room where he presses a button repeatedly and looks somewhat anxious.

'Je to kaput,' he says shaking his head and looking seriously concerned.

He holds up his hand showing five fingers and then points to his watch and disappears back to his own house. I wander back into our kitchen where Rob, who is now wearing his entire outdoor wardrobe, has cunningly positioned Sonya's bulk over his feet and is using Spaggy as a hot-water bottle.

'Any luck?' he asks.

'Oh my goodness, that was so embarrassing!'

'What was, love?'

I explain about our neighbours appearing in a state of semi-undress and, needless to say, Rob finds it highly amusing.

'Ha! You mean you interrupted something?'

'I've no idea. Maybe they were just getting dressed but they do seem to have a very casual attitude. I mean they didn't seem to be at all embarrassed.'

'What about the heating? Does Lubor think he can do anything?'

'I don't know, he's coming back in five minutes, but he used the word kaput so it doesn't sound very hopeful.'

A few minutes later Lenka arrives at the door, this time thankfully wearing a pair of ski-pants.

'Hello! I afraid my English not good,' she starts. 'Mmmmm. It very cold in house so please, you come to my house.'

Rob and I look at each other with slightly quizzical expressions. We realise that we can't really get out of this one.

'Dyakooee motz,' I reply, attempting to thank her.

But what about the dogs? We can hardly say, 'Oh, and would you mind if we bring Spaggy and Sonya with us?' Fortunately Lenka has already anticipated the problem and smiles kindly at us.

'And you bring dogs. It okay!'

So, twenty minutes later we're all sitting cosily in our neighbours' sitting-room, but, to our alarm and embarrassment, they have removed their trousers again and are back down to their underwear. They seem totally relaxed and oblivious to the fact that we're both feeling very uneasy about their state of undress. Even Rob seems perturbed by the somewhat casual, domestic set-up.

We attempt to make informal chit-chat with Lenka's rather limited vocabulary but this proves very restricting. After exchanging a few basic pieces of information about our respective lives Lenka is clearly searching for the words to relate a story to us. I smile at her encouragingly.

'When I am in England first time,' she begins, 'I speak no English. I am au pair to family. They very kind and very rich. The man he say to me, Lenka, if you have problem you go to police and you say, my name is Lenka I'm as daft as a brush.'

Rob and I collapse into fits of laughter imagining the poor girl following the advice.

'He bastard!' she laughs. 'He fucking bastard!'

Our jaws drop simultaneously and we stare at each other in horror, wondering if Lenka realises just how strong her language is.

'I go get biscuits,' she announces, getting up from her armchair and disappearing into the garage. She returns with a large tray of what are clearly home-made biscuits.

'Please. You eat,' she says, offering me a plate.

The smell of biscuits proves irresistible to the dogs and both of them start to pester us for a share of the feast. Spaggy is relentless but Sonya quickly accepts that she isn't going to get anything and wanders off down the passage to the back of the house.

'It okay!' says Lenka realising that I'm concerned about 70kg of slobbering fur wandering around her house.

However, it's only a few seconds later that a very excited, deep, throaty bark erupts from the far end of the passage. Spaggy immediately jumps up and scoots off to investigate what Sonya is barking about. He quickly joins in and by now I'm decidedly worried that something untoward is happening.

'Excuse me Lenka. I'll just go and get the dogs,' I say hurriedly and head off in the direction of the barking which seems to be coming from the bathroom.

My scream quickly alerts the entire household. I enter the bathroom to find both Spaggy and Sonya standing with their paws on the side of the bath, Spaggy struggling to see, but Sonya already in the act of climbing over the side.

'Chris? Are you alright? Whatever's the matter?' shouts Rob rushing into the bathroom to find out the cause of my distress.

'There's a bloody great fish in the bath!' I cry, trying not to let my shock result in tears.

'A fish?' he cries in disbelief.

'A carp. It's swimming around in the bath! I hate to say it Rob but I have a horrible feeling it might be their Christmas dinner.'

Lubor and Lenka appear and try their best to soothe me, clearly embarrassed by the event.

'Mmmm. No problem! Tomorrow we will eat fish!' says Lenka smiling and trying to calm me down. 'Please you must come eat dinner. You are welcome to have bed tonight in our house. It very cold in your house.'

I quickly perform a charade demonstrating a huge protest, indicating that we'll be tucked up in bed under the duvet with the dogs, I'm sure we'll be fine. So, after a welcome second cup of coffee, we retire to our abode accompanied by Spaggy and Sonya.

'Phew! That was a close one!' exclaims Rob. 'Do you think they were hoping we'd stay?'

'Goodness knows,' I reply. 'I don't know about you but I'm more than happy to hug a dog.'

And so we retire to bed along with Spaggy and Sonya who seem delighted that the house rules are being totally disregarded. The pair of them need no encouragement to climb onto the bed and snuggle up with us.

'It's doggy heaven,' I whisper to Rob.

'I know!' he replies cuddling into me.

Initially unable to sleep we spend the next half hour planning how to escape eating the carp. A feigned stomach upset, a sick dog, even accidentally-on-purpose letting our fishy dinner drop off our plate onto the floor and letting the dogs eat it seems too far-fetched. We realise that there's no way out, we're just going to have to eat the poor creature. And at that all four of us drift very quickly into dreamland.

Christmas Eve arrives and it's only then that we realise, embarrassingly, that we have no gifts to offer our neighbours.

'We have to give them something after all their kindness,' I protest.

'Yes, but what?' ask Rob. 'All the shops are shut now and we haven't got anything with us. We can hardly take them a half-empty bottle of wine.'

I try to consider the options. There must be something we can lay our hands on. We're not in the habit of exchanging gifts any more as we really feel that we've reached the stage in life where we don't need anything. However, we'd agreed, that in order to make Christmas Day just a bit special, we'd buy each other a little something for under a fiver.

'Well, I've got my present to you,' I declare.

'And I've got my present to you,' replies Rob.

'I guess we could just give them to Lubor and Lenka instead,' I suggest.

'Mmmm. Not such a good idea,' replies Rob looking slightly uneasy.

'Why not?'

'You'll have to wait until Christmas Day but I'm definitely not giving your present to Lenka.'

'In which case they'll just have to share yours.'

'Oh!' says Rob, obviously a bit put out.

'What was I going to get?'

'A box of your favourite Anthon Berg chocolates, apricots in brandy.'

'Oh no Chris! How could you?'

'Needs must!' I reply and head off to find the box that I'd carefully secreted in my suitcase.

After a very late breakfast, and having walked the dogs, we head next door. Poor little Spaggy is shaking with cold as the snow is now so deep that he acts like a miniature snow-plough, forcing his small frame through the powdery blanket that has come down overnight. From a distance we can only see the tip of his tail sticking up, proud of the snowfall.

'If it gets any deeper we'll have to attach a flag to his tail!' laughs Rob.

Lubor and Lenka greet us warmly and we're shown into the living room. To our relief they've actually got their clothes on but the house is in darkness. We wonder if they've had a power cut but obviously have no way of confirming the fact. Sonya embarrasses us by rolling over onto her back, stretching out her back legs and squirming around blissfully on the carpet. Her long back legs look almost human and we joke that she looks very like a man in a gorilla suit. Eventually she stops moving, falls asleep on her back and begins to snore, clearly enjoying the warmth of the underfloor heating. Spaggy curls up on Rob's lap and we sit in somewhat awkward silence. As our hosts have little understanding of English Rob and I are able to talk to one another without worrying too much about what we're saying, but attempt to be slightly cryptic just in case Lenka picks up on what it is we're discussing. Being December the days are very short so it isn't very long before we're sitting in total darkness. Lubor seems restless and keeps walking over to the window, looking up into the sky.

'Maybe he's looking for Father Christmas,' jokes Rob.

'Doubt it. It's baby Jesus who brings the presents over here. I know there's something about waiting to see a pig but I've never really understood it,' I muse.

'I shouldn't think he's going to see one in the sky!' laughs Rob.

Suddenly Lubor is clearly excited and beckons us over to the window. He points up into the heavens and says cheerily,

'Hvězda!'

At this he moves over to the door, reaches for the light switch and, bingo, we have light!

'I'm not sure what that was about,' puzzles Rob.

Lenka comes to our rescue.

'Mmm. It is star in sky. When we see star we have lights and we eat dinner.'

'Pity it hadn't been cloudy then we could have escaped the fish,' Rob mutters, turning to me.

I try hard not to laugh and have to stifle a giggle. Lenka disappears into the kitchen and, as she opens the door, the strong smell of fish wafts into the sitting room. Carp. Spaggy and Sonya wake up, noses twitching and head for the kitchen but I can already feel my throat tightening. Rob and I look sympathetically at each other. It's then that I recall the other finding of my research into Czech Christmas customs.

'By the way darling, I hate to alarm you,' I say quietly, 'but I read somewhere that they don't usually drink alcohol on Christmas Eve.'

I can see the look of horror spread over Rob's face.

'But it's Christmas!' he wails. 'Fish and no wine! I think I'd rather go back next door and freeze to death, at least we've got some alcohol.'

At this point Lubor stands up and ushers us to the table, disappears into the kitchen and returns clutching a large bottle of champagne. A huge smile spreads across Rob's face and we try not to appear too excited, however, the sight of a bottle of alcohol makes us both feel instantly more relaxed. It's then that we notice that we're all strangely seated towards one side of the table.

'Er, this is a bit cosy,' says Rob. 'You don't think they want to play footsie do you?'

I recall reading that it's bad luck to sit with your back to the door and guess that this strange custom explains the rather weird seating arrangement, so we're all left sitting awkwardly to one side when Lenka arrives with our first dish of wine sausages and potato salad. It's surprisingly good. We make appropriate appreciative noises but are quietly dreading the main course.

The carp actually looks more appealing than I'd imagined. It's been cut into slices, covered with bread-crumbs and fried. I try not to look anxious but I'm seriously concerned that one or both of us are going to disgrace ourselves when trying to swallow even a mouthful. The whole event is made worse by the fact that we'd made our lunch's acquaintance only yesterday.

'Dobrou chuť,' says Lubor, raising his glass. 'Na zdraví!'

'Na zdravi!' we reply.

The carp tastes foul. It has that nasty muddy taste that reminds me why I don't like fish that are bottom feeders. Clearly its time in the bath hasn't done much to improve the flavour. I adopt the technique of putting a forkful of fish in my mouth and then having a gulp of champagne. The combination helps to deaden the taste and wash it down more quickly. I smile and make encouraging noises but am afraid that being too enthusiastic might result in my being offered a second helping. Rob is clearly struggling and keeps kicking my leg and pulling silly faces which really doesn't help the situation. We both heave a sigh of relief when the plates are cleared and Lubor returns with a green bottle and four glasses.

'Becherovka!' he smiles, removes the top from the bottle and pours a measure into each glass.

We raise our glasses and, now in party mood, Rob cries out, 'Nádraží!'

I'm impressed that he's remembered the toast as I'm finding the language totally forgettable. However, Lubor and Lenka collapse into fits of laughter, Lenka trying hard not to choke on her drink.

'Did I say something funny?' asks Rob, giving me a slightly wounded look.

Lenka is still laughing but manages to splutter, 'You say railway station! It is Na zdraví! not Nádraží!' she cries.

We all have a good laugh and follow Lubor's example by knocking back the measure in one go. It's only then that we discover that this stuff is like the mouthwash they give you at the dentist's. It tastes strongly of cloves and clears the sinuses in one swig. We decline a second glass but before we can escape Lubor is already returning to the table with a different bottle.

'Slivovice!' he announces, removing the top and pouring a measure into each of our glasses. 'Nádraží!' he cries, raising his glass and laughing.

'Nádraží!' we reply and, not wanting to offend, knock back the contents of our glasses.

At least this tastes okay. In fact it's really quite nice but clearly very potent. I can see that Rob's getting a taste for the stuff but know from experience that him having one too many is a really bad idea.

'I think we'd better get these dogs out for their last walk before it gets too late Rob,' I hint, giving him one of my best glares.

'Don't worry darling,' he replies, 'they'll be fine for a while yet. It isn't that late.'

And at that Lubor pours the pair of them another slivovice. I can see where this is going to end.

It's almost an hour later when I eventually manage to extract Rob and help him stagger back to the house, having handed Lubor and Lenka the box of chocolates.

'We could at least have stayed until they opened them,' Rob complains as we stumble through the snow with the dogs, Rob finding it difficult to remain upright. 'I might have had just one. One teensy-weensy little choccy.'

'Never mind Mr Grumpy. 'Tis the season of goodwill. You'll

just have to wait until we get back home. Speaking of presents, when do I get to open mine?'

'Not until the morning,' he slurs with a lop-sided grin.

I wake up early, half hanging out of the bed with a huge, furry paw pressed up against my cheek as Sonya has somehow managed to take over most of my side. I reach over to Rob only to find his side of the bed empty. I'm half expecting to find him crashed out on the floor so I'm hugely surprised when my lovely man appears carrying a cup of tea. I'm frankly amazed that he isn't either unconscious or throwing up in the bathroom.

'Happy Christmas darling,' he says, handing me a small package. 'Sorry it isn't anything bigger but I didn't have much room in my case.'

I sit up, eagerly tear off the Christmas wrapping paper and burst into fits of laughter.

'Knickers!' I shout. 'You bought me knickers!'

'Now you know why I didn't think it would be a good idea to give Lenka your present,' he laughs.

# 8

## WHAT THE CAT DRAGGED IN

'THE CATS ARE EASILY looked after, but don't be alarmed if Arthur jumps on the back of the milk-float in the morning,' Mary informs us as we sit down round the kitchen table to check a few details before she and her husband leave. 'He likes to ride up to the farm and back every day, it started when he was a kitten, but Thatcher won't stray far. It's so good of you to help us out like this. We were so worried about putting them in the cattery because Arthur goes off his food and we generally come back to a bag of bones. I'm sure he'll be much happier staying here at home. But he is a horror. He gets up to all sorts of mischief.'

'His favourite trick,' interrupts Dick, 'is to climb in through next door's bedroom window at night in the summer and sleep on their bed. Needless to say he's not too popular!'

Dick and Mary are retired teachers, both with a background in special needs. Retirement has been long-awaited and they're keen to make the most of it. Having shown us around the house and garden, they bid us goodbye and set off to Suffolk to meet their new grand-child for the first time.

'They seem a nice couple,' says Rob after they've left, 'and the cats seem easy enough. Mind you, I didn't like to ask how on earth Thatcher got his name. You don't suppose they were fans do you?'

'Apparently he was a rescue cat,' I reply. 'His owner had to go into a home and wasn't allowed to take him with her, so you can't hold Dick and Mary responsible for his name. But it's so horrid, isn't it, having to give up an animal like that? It's a pity that care homes can't be more accommodating.'

'And apartments,' says Rob. 'Remember when Pete was trying to find a flat? No-one would let him rent with a dog in tow. It took him months to find somewhere to live.'

'Well that's one of the reasons why there are so many homeless people with dogs on the streets these days,' I reply. 'It's impossible for them to find somewhere to live and, understandably, they don't want to give up their animal. It's so sad.'

Our new home is a black and white timber-framed cottage in the centre of a beautiful, conservation village in Shropshire. It's delightful, and the surrounding countryside offers lots of good walking country. Arthur and Thatcher are curious about their new guardians and eye us up warily before deigning to sit with us. However, it isn't long before Thatcher has clearly decided we're okay as he's taken to sitting on Rob's shoulder and sucking his hair. This is rather off-putting at first but we quickly come to terms with the fact that it's just what Thatcher does. He then manoeuvres himself onto Rob's lap and begins kneading his thighs with his paws and dribbling, clearly contented.

Arthur, a handsome ginger tom, keeps his distance and chooses to position himself in places that enable him to look down on us. When outside he appears mysteriously like the Cheshire Cat, peering down from the canopy of a tree, the roof of the cottage or, even more precariously, from the top of a wooden clothes prop. He's developed a curious hunting technique, in fact, if you observe him carefully, you wouldn't even know he was hunting. We find him staring at a patch of grass, totally transfixed. He sits absolutely still and refuses to be distracted. After two hours he's still sitting staring at the same spot on the lawn. Then wham! A white-socked paw conjures a mole out of thin air. Quite how he's managed to kill the poor creature remains a mystery, but he proves frighteningly swift and accurate. However, it seems that moles aren't good to eat and now the hunt is over Arthur proudly picks up his trophy in his mouth, walks over to the cottage and dumps the unfortunate creature ceremoniously on the doorstep. I go to thank him for the present and he rubs up against my legs, purring loudly, before disappearing into the kitchen for a nap.

'Gosh! That was amazing to witness,' says Rob, still taken aback by the experience. 'However did he manage it?'

'I have no idea but the poor mole didn't stand a chance did it? Here, come and have a look at him.'

It isn't often you get the chance to see a mole at such close quarters and this is a mole that demands inspection. Not only does he have huge front feet but he's curiously white, not grey, and has a ginger snout and ginger tummy. He clearly isn't an albino but more of an oddity. Not really knowing what to do with the corpse we decide to put it in a box out of reach of the cats while we go to the pub for lunch.

According to one of our guide-books The Three Horseshoes was voted County Pub of the Year by CAMRA five years ago, so, needless to say, Rob feels obliged to check it out. We head off up the lane to sample the local ale but are suddenly aware of a loud 'miaow' and, looking back, discover that Arthur has decided to join us.

'No Arthur, go home!' shouts Rob.

Arthur walks up and rubs his side along Rob's leg.

'Go home you silly boy, you can't come for a walk!'

But Arthur is not to be dissuaded. He trots along behind us then climbs up a high wall that runs parallel to the road and continues to walk alongside us until we reach the pub.

'Well you can't come in. You're just going to have to stay there fella,' Rob tells him as we head for the lounge.

Finding the door locked we make for the entrance to the bar. The interior is incredibly dark and filled with dense wood-smoke that's billowing out from an inglenook fireplace at the end of the room. The walls are a rather unpleasant shade of ochre and we're not quite sure if they've been painted that colour deliberately or if it's the nicotine-stained décor of yesteryear. The place is empty and there doesn't seem to be anyone serving. The smoke from the fire is causing us both to have coughing fits which fortunately act as a signal to the landlord that he actually has some customers. A large, decidedly miserable-looking man sporting a sweat-stained t-shirt appears from behind the bar. He has a huge stomach that hangs over the belt of his trousers and there are beads of perspiration rolling down his forehead.

'Yes?' enquires our host, lifting his forearm to catch some of the sweat that's now dripping off the end of his nose.

'I think we'll try two halves of Postman's Knock please,' says Rob.

His polite request is met with a cold silence as two halves are pulled from the pump and dumped on the counter. Without so much as a glance in our direction our barman slopes back through the door behind him, leaving us to sup our beer.

'Well, he'll go down a storm on TripAdvisor,' whispers Rob. 'It seems that things have gone a tad downhill in the last five years!'

We take our halves over to the far end of the room in order to escape the smoke and sit down on a huge, but rather uncomfortable, wooden settle under the window. We're greeted by a loud miaow and look up to find a distraught Arthur outside, pawing furiously at the glass.

'Oh bless him, he wants to come in!' says Rob.

'Well he can't and I certainly don't think Happy Larry would want him in here.'

'Okay, well let's drink up and go,' suggests Rob. 'I don't think my eyes can take much more of the smoke anyhow.'

He leaves the money for our drinks on the bar and we head outside only to discover that there's no sign of Arthur.

'He must have taken himself home,' says Rob. 'I expect he'll be waiting for his dinner when we get back.'

Except he isn't. We wander round the cottage searching

under beds and behind curtains but he's nowhere to be seen.

'He'll turn up, don't worry,' I say reassuringly.

Rob still hasn't got used to the comings and goings of cats and tends to get twitchy when they're not around. I can see him fretting.

'It's what cats do darling. He's probably stopped off at the farm to go mousing.'

We've often discussed having our own cat but Rob knows that his anxiety about their welfare would undermine the pleasure that having our very own feline would bring. By bedtime there's still no sign of Arthur, but Thatcher's enjoying the extra attention as Rob is using him as a comfort blanket.

'I'll just do one more round outside,' says Rob reaching for the torch.

Ten minutes later he's back looking despondent.

'There's not much else we can do love,' I say, trying to console him. 'He's probably gorging on something and'll show up later.'

Except he doesn't. By ten o'clock the following morning even I'm getting worried. We decide to set off in different directions to search for him. I'm secretly worried that he might have been hit by a car but don't want to plant the idea in Rob's head as he's fretting enough already. We agree that Rob will do the path across the field to the farm and I'll retrace our steps back to the pub.

I walk slowly back up the lane, my eyes scanning the hedges, knowing from bitter experience that folk sometimes knock a cat over and then leave the body at the side of the road. I'd once had to retrieve one of my own from the grass verge where I'd found her. Somehow dealing with the demise of someone else's cat seems a great deal worse, yet I know there's nothing we could have done to prevent an accident.

Having reached the end of the lane I arrive in the pub car park which is, not surprisingly, empty. A quick scout around and there's no sign of our furry friend. Then suddenly,

'Wow!' I hear. 'Wow, wow, wow!'

It's a very anxious wow and, as I turn the corner of the building, there, sitting on the same window-sill where we'd seen him the previous night, is dear Arthur, looking both distressed and dishevelled.

'Arthur! Here sweetheart. Oh you lovely boy, did you think we were still in there? Have you been out here all night?'

I reach out to him and he purrs like a washing-machine on fast spin and head-butts me in the face.

'Come on fella,' I say lifting him gently into my arms. 'We're going home.'

He struggles a bit, embarrassed by his loss of dignity, and ends up climbing onto my shoulders, but seems quite happy about staying there while I walk triumphantly back to the cottage. Rob has already returned and is overjoyed to see the boy again.

'You rascal!' he cries happily. 'You had me so worried! Where did you find him?'

I tell Rob and we realise that we'd probably inadvertently taken dear Arthur outside his familiar territory and that he was convinced that we were still in the pub.

'The next time we go there I suggest we leave him locked in the cottage and close the cat-flap,' says Rob firmly.

'You mean there's going to be a next time?' I laugh, rolling my eyes. 'Wasn't one visit enough?'

The following day I pop over to the village shop which is strangely housed in the church. Manned by volunteers, it serves the local community and is a welcome amenity in such a rural setting and saves us having to drive miles just to get a pint of milk. We've been made very welcome by the villagers that we've met and it's while I'm there that I happen to mention our white mole.

'Oh, Mr Coxon would be interested in that, he's our local

mole-catcher,' says the lady behind the counter. 'He lives next door here, you could give him a knock. I'm sure he'd be keen to see it.'

So, having returned the shopping to the house, I retrieve the mole from its box and wander over to Mr Coxon's cottage. The garden is immaculate, the rows of vegetables manicured to perfection, the hedges clipped into ingenious patterns of topiary and the lawn bordered by a razor-sharp edge. It's the old blacksmith's forge and, with roses round the door, is every inch the quintessential English cottage.

I announce my arrival by banging loudly on the door with the iron door-knocker. After a short wait, an extremely tall man, most probably in his eighties, dressed in a three-piece, tweed suit complete with pocket-watch, opens the door and stoops to greet me. He's the epitome of the English country gentleman. I introduce myself and explain the reason for my visit, holding out the mole for his inspection.

'Well, in all my years I've never seen one like this,' he muses. 'Albino, yes, but never one with this red colouring. How unusual! Thank you so much for bringing it for me to see.'

'Have you been catching moles for many years?' I ask, intrigued to know more.

'Mmm. Let me see, must be getting on for eighty,' he replies with a twinkle in his eye.

'My goodness, that's a lot of moles,' I laugh.

'There was one day,' he reminisces, 'when I was on my way home after collecting the moles from the traps that I'd set, when I bumped into Ivor Watkins' wife. That woman never stopped talking and was a dreadful gossip,' he smiles. 'Between you and me, while she was rabbiting on I quietly took one of the moles out of my pocket and slipped it into her shopping basket!'

I watch him laugh at what is clearly still a very strong memory.

'And then,' he continues chuckling to himself, 'I tipped my

hat, said my good morning and went home to wait for her scream!'

My jaw drops as I cannot imagine a gentleman like Mr Coxon playing such a naughty trick, but I can't help but see the funny side and we both end up in fits of laughter on his doorstep. I return to the cottage and relate the story to Rob.

'What a wicked thing to do!' he chuckles. 'You see, appearances can be deceptive. Speaking of which you'll never believe what I've got to tell you!'

'Go on then,' I say taking a seat in the rocking-chair after first removing Thatcher.

'Well, Mary had kindly left us some brochures and tourist info in the sitting room, and I was having a browse while you were out. There's one leaflet specifically about the village here and an article about the pub. You'll never believe it, but not only did it once win CAMRA's County Pub of the Year, it seems that Happy Larry was voted Best Landlord!'

'What?' I cry in disbelief. 'You're having me on Rob. Best Landlord? Oh come on, the village must have been taking the mickey. Perhaps they did it deliberately to give him a wake-up call or maybe there simply weren't any other candidates.'

'I think we ought to go and congratulate him!' suggests Rob. 'Fancy a pint?'

# 9

# BARKING AT THE MOON

'What about this Rob?' I hint subtly one evening. "The main responsibilities will be to look after our two lovable dogs, Dillon and Winston. Dillon is a one year-old Lakeland Terrier and Winston, a nine year-old black lab. The sit would suit a couple who can continue the training that we have started with Dillon and are able to give the dogs plenty of attention during their stay. Our house is a comfortable cottage just outside Bradford-on-Avon with a large, enclosed garden and an orchard. We're close to some outstanding countryside with walks from our door but within easy reach of supermarkets, National Trust properties etc.'"

'Yes, if you want, I'm game. Go for it,' replies Rob in his usual enthusiastic manner, without lifting his head from his book. So I do.

Liz and I had been in contact for some weeks prior to our sit, exchanging information and firming up the details for our arrival. She'd warned me that she'd be returning from a weekend hen party in Bristol the same day that we'd be arriving, having been away for a few days with some girl-friends in her campervan, Daisy. It was therefore rather odd to pass a rather hippyish, beaten-up old VW on the road just a day before our arrival, festooned with white daisies.

'I wonder if that was Daisy?' I ask Rob looking back down the road. 'That'd be a strange coincidence, passing her on the way wouldn't it?'

'Yes, apart from the fact that we're miles from Bristol and that van was heading in the wrong direction,' my man replies clearly despairing at my somewhat skewed sense of direction.

Daisy it most certainly wasn't because, as we pull into Liz and Nigel's drive the next evening, Rob finds it quite a challenge to manoeuvre the car past the enormous Hymer motorhome that's occupying most of the courtyard. No sooner have we shut the car doors than our hosts are at the front door to greet us, wine glasses in hand.

'Hello! Welcome!' cries Liz, rushing out to do that kissy kissy thing that's become fashionable in recent years.

We still find this a little too intimate a greeting on first meeting but Rob doesn't seem to be objecting on this occasion.

'Please, come in,' she continues, but is having to shout above the manic barking that's coming from a room at the back of the house. 'That's Dillon!' she continues. 'I'm afraid he always barks at people, it's a terrier thing.'

Liz's long, blonde hair is piled up in an untidy chignon, a style that I've often attempted but never quite mastered, her legs clad in a pair of psychedelic leggings and her feet in a pair of Ug boots, all of this presumably customary garb for hen parties. Nigel, on the other hand, looks somewhat older and is dressed in a much more conservative manner, his checked shirt covered by a knitted waistcoat, his cords, I cannot help but note, fastened by a safety-pin. He looks every inch a pipe and slippers man.

'Do have a glass,' Liz says warmly, as we process into the sitting room. 'We've already started. I've only just got back from Bristol and shit, we're off tomorrow morning at six. I must be mad,' she laughs, thrusting her glass towards Nigel for him to fill. 'Anyhow, let's give you a tour of the house and then you can meet the dogs. They're so excited!'

It's a beautiful house, stylish without being fussy and with a wholesome, homely air about it. There are some impressive, abstract paintings on the walls and quirky ornaments in garish colours adorn various pieces of beautifully-crafted, modern furniture.

too happy about being left behind. I wander down to make a cup of tea and then head back to bed. In an instant Dillon flies up the stairs, bounds through the bedroom door and leaps up onto the bed. A loud groan sounds from under the duvet.

'It's your early morning wake-up call,' I laugh.

Rob turns over and buries his head under the pillow. I rather like our new furry friend but clearly being allowed on the bed is not a good idea, although I suspect he gets his own way when Liz and Nigel are around. I eventually manage to get him back downstairs to the kitchen where I close the door and return to the bedroom.

'How're you feeling?' I ask Rob as his head appears tentatively from under the covers.

'Lousy,' is the mumbled reply.

'Well we did have a lot to drink last night,' I smile looking at the tousled head beside me. 'Nice people though. Liz seems great fun. Nigel's good company too but tell me, why did you spend all evening calling him Ian?'

'Oh God, did I?' groans Rob.

'Afraid so. I did try to give you a couple of my best withering looks but you were too far gone. I shouldn't worry about it, he probably didn't even notice.'

I wander through to the en suite bathroom to have a shower but can't help noticing the unmade bed and the discarded clothing on the bedroom floor. A pair of rather slinky black knickers have been abandoned by the foot of the bed and an equally exotic bra hung over the back of a chair. I wonder whether I should put them somewhere out of sight before Rob takes a shower, but feel that it would be rather improper to go around handling someone else's undergarments. My M&S matching set seems suddenly drab by comparison. When Rob arrives in the kitchen for breakfast I try to ignore the rather smug grin on his face.

While we attempt to eat our muesli Dillon continues his

manic barking and is certainly not helping Rob's headache. He really is a true terrier in every sense of the word. 'Curious, intense and impulsive,' says Google. Well, they got that right! He has to know exactly what's going on, where everyone is and what they're doing and when he becomes fixated on something there is absolutely no way of stopping him doing what he wants to do. Any intervention is met with a very threatening, throaty growl which leaves you feeling that if you go any further he's going to take your hand off. Yet this dog is a bundle of love and likes nothing more than to suddenly jump into your arms (literally, which is quite alarming on the first occasion) and give you a full facial. I try to cast aside all thoughts of where his tongue was less than five minutes ago.

"This breed has keen vision and acute hearing and can be counted on to sound the alert when anything is amiss, sometimes even when nothing is amiss, but might be in the future!" reports Google. Nothing could be more true. Dillon barks at the postman, delivery men, cars, lorries, tractors, the neighbours, the neighbours' dogs, aeroplanes, birds, squirrels, us, and constantly at poor Winston. His hearing is so acute that he picks up on sounds several seconds before we do then proceeds to bark, loudly and unceasingly. He is driving us nuts.

Winston, on the other hand, is the model labrador, but a long-suffering target of Dillon's grumpy nature. As a puppy Dillon is still learning the ropes but Winston is such a gentle-natured soul that he's completely overruled by Mr Grumpy. Winston's happy to play, but anything he manages to get in his soft mouth, Dillon immediately wants. Dillon quickly, and noisily, lets us know that that is his stick, his ball, his chewy, his squeaky toy, and in particular, his bone!

Around doggy feeding-time I retreat to the boot room to prepare their food. Keeping to Liz's instructions I leave Dillon in the kitchen while I feed Winston, then return to the kitchen with Dillon's food which I set down in front of him. A pair of sad eyes look at the dish and then up at me.

'There you are Dillon, there's your dinner!' I say cheerily.

Dillon looks again at his dish and back at me.

'Good boy! Have your dinner!'

Dillon doesn't move. This is a first for me. I have yet to meet a dog that doesn't eat unless ill, especially once given permission.

'Mmm. Yummy!' I say getting down to his level. 'I wish I was having that!'

Dillon looks decidedly mournful and I wonder if this might be the first dog ever to go off his food because his owners have gone away. He lies down on his bed, puts his head on his paws and stares up at me looking horribly sad. I reason that maybe he needs a command so send a quick text off to Liz. 'What is command to get Dillon to eat?' A couple of minutes later, just as Rob arrives, I get a reply.

'Who're you texting?' he asks.

'Liz, but I think she must have been on the wine again,' I reply. 'She's just written, "I using to say good on their but he something doesn't ed." It's not too helpful.'

'Why, is there a problem?' asks Rob.

'Dillon's not eating but I think it might be because I haven't given him the right command. I was trying to establish what Liz usually says to him. He must be hungry by now poor lad.'

I sit down on the floor and, rather reluctantly, scoop up a handful of wet dog-food in my hand and hold it under his nose. He's immediately alert and wolfs down my offering then looks expectantly at me, clearly wanting more. Three handfuls later I'm beginning to regret starting this game but at the same time I'm relieved that we've got some food down him.

As Rob is still suffering from his hangover, I take the risk of walking the dogs on my own. They're both clearly happy to be out and, being familiar with the paths across the fields, are able to lead me round their normal circuit. The meadow is thick with lush grass and wild flowers. I'm thrilled to see orchids growing in abundance as well as corn-cockle and cowslips, plants that have joyfully started to make a come-back after being under threat of disappearance. Winston ambles along happily by my side while Dillon bounces through the long grass looking more like a pronking deer than a dog. His energy seems to be boundless and I'm exhausted just by watching him. After a good, long walk I manage to get the pair of them back on their leads and head back to the house where Rob is still nursing a headache.

The next morning we realise that we're in urgent need of supplies so plan a trip to the nearest supermarket in order to stock up. According to the notes that have been provided the dogs should be fine on their own for a couple of hours and anyhow, we don't intend being out all that long. We settle them down in their baskets with a chew each and collect our bags before heading for the door.

'Security code,' I remind Rob.

'Yep, got it here,' he replies reaching for a bit of paper. 'It's just as well I wrote it down because I don't even remember the conversation the other night.'

He enters the numbers into the key pad and closes the door. Success! I have to confess that these systems terrify me as I'm always anticipating something going wrong. So, intruder alarm set, we head off to the supermarket.

It may sound silly to confess that I actually get excited by new supermarkets as they have so many more lines than we do at home, so I always enjoy browsing the aisles and buying new stuff. It's therefore a bit later than anticipated when we return to the house, our bags loaded with provisions for our stay. Pulling into the drive we can already hear Dillon barking furiously. Having unloaded the shopping from the car we approach the front door. Rob hesitates.

'Something wrong?' I ask.

'Mmmmm,' replies Rob. 'I hate to say it but I've forgotten the code for the alarm.'

'Okay,' I reply, trying very hard to keep my cool. 'Let's think this through. Are you sure you can't remember it?'

'Afraid not,' replies Rob looking suitably embarrassed.

'But you had it written on a bit of paper before we left darling. What happened to it?'

'I wrote the shopping list on the back of the same bit of paper and left it in the trolley. I was sure I'd remember it.'

I'm trying desperately to remain calm and consider our options. We can drive back to the supermarket (a 40 minute round trip) in the hope of finding the bit of paper (unlikely) or we can have a wild guess at the code and face the consequences if we get it wrong (alerting the neighbours and the local police force and getting a one-star review from the owners, none of which is sounding too good.)

'Okay. So we know that it's Liz's age. So how old do you reckon she is?' I ask.

'I'd guess about forty-eight,' replies Rob.

'Rubbish!' I reply indignantly, 'she must be at least fifty-five!'

'I wouldn't have thought so,' replies Rob. 'If she is then she's in pretty good shape!'

'Oh, I see! So she's forty-eight is she? Well you can punch the numbers in the key-pad and on your head be it if you get it wrong.'

The barking from inside the house has reached such a pitch that both Winston and the neighbours' dogs are now joining in the protest.

'I suppose I'm going to have to ring Liz and ask her,' I shout above the din.

The signal in the area is poor but it's the only way that I can see out of this mess. I dial the number and wait for the international dialling tone.

'Shit! Her phone's switched off. We're snookered!'

'No! Hang on a minute! I've just had a thought,' says Rob excitedly.

'It'd better be a good one Robert,' I reply, by now beginning to feel more than a little tetchy.

My dear husband, who has clearly been seduced by our hostess, is insistent that she's at least seven years younger than she clearly is and has managed to get us locked out of the house.

'We're not locked out darling, we're just temporarily homeless,' says Rob smiling sweetly but I recognise the anxiety in his face.

'Yes, and we have the choice of spending the night in the car while the dogs starve to death or alerting the local police force to the situation. I can just imagine the scenario. 'So tell me Madam, what is the name of the people who own the house?' Rob, we don't even know their surname, we'd probably be arrested under suspicion of burglary.'

'Calm down, calm down, it's okay,' says Rob trying to pacify me, 'I think I know where I might've put the shopping list. I think I might have dropped it into the bottom of one of the shopping baskets when we were at the cash-out, not in the trolley.'

We immediately start to empty the contents of five carrier-bags of food all over the front doorstep. It is, of course, the last bag that contains the shopping list, now somewhat soggy as the frozen peas that have been sitting on top of it have started to melt.

'Yay!' shouts Rob in triumph. 'Got it!' and skips round the courtyard, waving the paper aloft in his hand.

'Come on then, what's the number?' I demand.

'5353,' comes the somewhat reluctant reply.

My anger instantly turns to smugness, 'Robert Baird, you owe me one! Forty-eight my foot! Now get that bloody door open and fast.'

Needless to say the dogs are delighted to see us and we're greeted excitedly the minute the door is open. Dillon heads off for an urgent pee and a few circuits of the garden, barking manically at imaginary intruders, while Winston goes for a sniff round the bushes, keen to be out in the air. We head for the kitchen with a couple of the bags and collapse on the bar stools.

'I think we deserve a drink!' says Rob, lifting two glasses out of the cupboard and grabbing a half-empty bottle from the fridge. 'Cheers darling!' he says, handing me a welcome glass of slightly flat Prosecco.

'Cheers sweetheart,' I reply smiling. 'Well I'm glad that's all over, what a day we've had!'

I drain my glass in one, even flat bubbly tasting good.

'Er, just a thought. Have you seen the dogs?' I ask.

'No, they were both outside when we came in, I'd better go and round them up, it's almost time for their dinner anyhow,' says Rob and disappears to find them. Within seconds he's back, flushed and panting.

'What's the matter?' I ask.

'It's the dogs. I don't think they're going to need feeding. They've been helping themselves to the contents of the shopping bags that we abandoned on the doorstep.'

'Oh no, I forgot all about the other bags!' I shriek.

My mind immediately starts to go through the 'Foods Dangerous to Dogs' checklist. Chocolate (one bar of, Rob's Lindt 70% daily treat); Currants, sultanas and raisins (Dundee fruit loaf); onions (one packet of Waitrose soffrito mixture); avocado (two ready to eat); grapes (one bunch of). I snatch what's left of the remaining bags and run frantically back into the house to try and work out what the pair of them have eaten. To my huge relief I work out that they've helped themselves to two sirloin steaks, a packet of frozen chips and half a pound of butter, complete with wrapper. I guess it could be worse but only time will tell.

Having put our purchases well out of the way of the dogs, we collapse in a heap while I try to muster the energy to cook dinner. I'm suddenly alerted by the sound of my mobile ringing.

'International' says the caller name. I prepare myself for the worst.

'Bonsoir Christine! Ça va?' shouts a rather drunken voice from across the water.

'Ah, Liz! Bonsoir. Ça va bien merci,' I reply, looking at Rob and rolling my eyes.

'Oh good. I saw that you'd tried to ring and we were worried that there might have been a problem avec les chiens.'

'Oh no, everything's fine. Don't worry. I was just trying to ring you to reassure you that we were all okay,' I reply. 'Dillon's eating really well now and Winston seems fine.'

'Oh that is good news, we guessed they'd be okay. Nous sommes about to have dinner but I thought I'd better telephoner just in case. We're just enjoying a glass of argnamac,' she slurs. 'Anyhow, glad tout va bien! Love to the woofties. Bonne nuit!'

'Bonne nuit,' I reply as Winston throws up in the kitchen.

# 10

# HOPPING MAD

'SO WHO, OR WHAT, IS Patrick?' quizzes Rob one morning at breakfast.

'He's a rabbit.'

'A rabbit? Chris, I don't know the first thing about rabbits. Are you sure this is a good idea?'

'We'd be fine. Rabbits don't do much and it'll mean that we can get out and about to explore instead of being tied to walking a dog and we can have a lie in in the mornings. As long as their hutch is cleaned out regularly and given food and water there's not much that can go wrong. The ones I had when I was little were lovely. I even used to take Melvin for walks.'

'Melvin? You called a rabbit Melvin?'

'Well no, not me. I took him on when a friend didn't want him any more. He lived in an old tea chest in our garden shed. I used to let him out for a hop around the garden in his run but he was never any trouble. I used to take him round to our neighbour's garden to help her pollinate her apple trees. We used to carry him round and use his tail to spread the pollen. Nothing better for the job than a rabbit's tail apparently.'

'Mmm. I'm still not sold on the idea. It isn't one of those house rabbits is it?'

'No, he lives outside in a hutch. I used to let Melvin into the house but he used to hide behind the television and chew the wires.'

'So where exactly does Patrick live?'

'Alderney.'

'Alderney? You want to go to Alderney to look after a rabbit? No Chris, I'm not keen. I really can't see the point. I'm a dog man and besides, we'd have to fly. You know I don't like those small planes, they terrify me and I'd be sick.'

Three weeks later we're waiting on the tarmac to board the Aurigny Trislander to our neighbouring island. As our names are called I pick up on the fact that the air steward is eyeing each of us up with a view to distributing the weight evenly across the plane. We dutifully haul ourselves aboard alongside the other passengers. Our bags are put at the back of the plane along with five large boxes of bananas. The seating arrangements are a bit cosy but it all adds to the fun.

'It's a good job we're not travelling with a team of rugby players or we'd never get off the ground!' I jest, but Rob, who's already looking pale, clearly isn't in a joking mood.

The doors are slammed shut and we go through the safety regulations. This involves our pilot turning round in his seat and addressing us from the open cock-pit. He recommends that we remain seated for the duration of the flight which raises a smile from the passengers as there's no aisle on these tiny aircraft. We're all sitting two abreast in something akin to a large cigar tube. Rob's already going into high anxiety mode, constantly wringing his hands and breathing heavily. As we taxi towards the runway he grabs hold of my arm and I can feel his nails digging into me. I notice that the emergency handle on the window is sealed with a strip of silicone and that the inner skin of the fuselage has started coming apart in places, but choose not to alert him to the fact. Unable to converse because of the noise level I smile at him reassuringly and squeeze his hand as the plane starts to accelerate and we leave the runway, wobbling slightly in the cross-wind. Soon we're flying over the cliff edge where our plane dips suddenly before heading out over the sea. Alderney is already visible in front of us, a misty, grey rock on the horizon and, as we approach the coast, we can see a frenzied cloud of gannets circling below on Les Etacs. Because of the cross-wind we have to touch down on the grass so our landing proves a bit bumpy, but we're thankfully on the ground and I can see the relief on Rob's face.

The airport is no more than a collection of huts, but it's a surprisingly busy little place. Having collected our bags off the conveyor belt that dumps the luggage unceremoniously in a heap on the floor, we head for the car park. A short, plump lady and a gentleman with a beard that would make Father Christmas proud, are there waiting and give us a friendly wave, their faces beaming.

'Christine, Robert, welcome to Alderney!' shouts the lady. 'Hello, I'm Marie and this is my husband Alan. I hope you had a good flight?'

'Yes, thanks,' replies Rob, managing a smile but still looking a tad washed-out after our crossing.

We duly follow our hosts across the car park to a very grubby, pick-up truck.

'I'm afraid we don't have anything glamorous,' says Alan apologetically. 'The salt air wrecks vehicles over here, it's simply not worth wasting your money on anything decent. Do climb aboard.'

We scramble over what appears to be several months' worth of discarded sweet-wrappers, empty coke cans and mouldy sandwich-boxes. I'm now quietly worried about what the house is going to be like. Squashed in the back seat we enjoy the drive down the hill to the coast and on to St Anne's and our new home.

To my relief the cottage is both clean and tidy. A cute, brightly-painted building just off the High Street.

'You've got everything on your doorstep so no worries about shopping,' Alan informs us. 'There's a small supermarket just down the road where you can get just about everything and there are plenty of places to eat out, or take-aways if you prefer to have a night off cooking. Oh, and I've left our contact numbers beside the phone in case you need to get hold of us.'

'And the vet if we needed one?' asks Rob.

'Just round the corner but the hours are a bit erratic. There's usually a nurse on duty but the vet only flies in every couple of weeks or for emergencies. Their number's on the information sheet. Anyhow, you should be fine with Patrick. We've never had any problems with him, touch wood. Here, come out the back and say hello to the little fellow.'

'So how come you have a rabbit?' I ask, curious to know how a couple in their seventies have ended up with the sort of pet that children normally have.

'We found him on the common about four months ago on St Patrick's day, hence his name,' replies Marie. 'He was clearly injured and looking pretty pathetic, he must have been attacked by a dog, or more likely a cat, so we brought him home. He's been with us ever since as we're too nervous of letting him go back into the wild and besides, we've become rather fond of him. The trouble is that we hadn't thought about the fact that we wouldn't be able to travel without finding someone to look after him, which is where you good folk come in.'

'So has Patrick been, er, done?' I ask tentatively, bending down to inspect our new charge.

'No, we didn't see the need really, and as we don't have any other rabbits it isn't really an issue,' replies Alan.

I don't like to comment on the fact that I understood that bucks that are still intact can be aggressive. Hopefully this one will prove friendly.

And so, having said our goodbyes the following morning, we venture out to feed Patrick. He's a sweet little thing, and still very tiny. However he's happy to be stroked through the wire of his cage and clearly likes his grub. We fill his bowl with fresh water, top up his food and hay and soon he's munching happily.

'Is that it then?' asks Rob.

'Well yes, apart from mucking him out regularly what else

did you think we'd have to do?'

'Nothing I guess but they're a bit boring then, rabbits. I mean they just sit there and eat or sleep.'

'No they're not. They're affectionate and fun. My rabbit used to lie by my side in the garden and sunbathe.'

'You mean Melvin?'

'No, not Melvin. That one was Thumper.'

'You certainly had some original names for your pets,' scoffs Rob.

'She used to thump the ground with her back feet if she was nervous about something. That's why I called her Thumper. Anyhow, let's go and explore. I could do with a good hike. It's ages since we had a decent walk.'

We amble down the hill and along to the common where we stop off at the bird-hide to see if there are any interesting visitors. It's well-known that the island often attracts rare species that stop off for a rest having flown long distances over the sea. Sadly not today. Apart from a few sparrows and a couple of blue-tits we see nothing but a rather bedraggled heron. We sit quietly watching him, poised on one leg, admiring his reflection, but decide to make our way back to the house rather than get cold. We find Patrick sitting with his side pressed up against the wire of his hutch, nose twitching.

'Marie did say we could let him out any time Rob. He can't escape from the garden because of that high wall and he needs to get some exercise. It's unfair to leave him cooped up and he must be bored.'

'If you say so,' says Rob and unlatches the hooks that hold the door of the hutch in place.

Patrick sniffs the air for a while then hops daintily onto the concrete of the enclosed yard. After a couple of investigative circuits he jumps up onto the dwarf wall that contains the flower borders and starts to munch the leaves of some of the plants. In fact what he's doing is simply biting through the stalks of the flowers and letting them collapse.

'Maybe this wasn't such a good idea Chris. He's going to destroy the border if we keep him out much longer.'

'I guess you're right, you'd better put him back in his hutch then.'

'I'd better put him back? Why me? You're the rabbit expert round here.'

Rob walks towards our furry friend, hands outstretched, but Patrick immediately hops away from him, leaps off the wall and snuggles down in a sunny corner of the yard. Rob approaches him again slowly but Patrick has already caught on and skedaddles back to the flowerbed.

'Maybe it would be better if you caught him,' he says.

I walk up to Patrick, scoop him up in my hands and pop him back in his hutch.

'You just need to move quickly and be confident. Anyhow, it must be wine o'clock. Let's open a bottle.'

We spend the next couple of days walking the cliffs and the beaches. It's wonderful to be somewhere so peaceful and a joy to have open spaces to enjoy, albeit a bit bleak in places.

'I really like it here Rob. It's lovely to get away from the traffic and the built-up clutter at home. I rather like the open landscape. I know there isn't much to do but I'd rather live in Alderney than back in the UK.'

It's the next day that the rain arrives, cold, heavy and constant. The sky is leaden and the wind has got up. A rather eerie howling emanates from the fireplace as the force of the wind sucks at the chimney-pot, at times making it difficult to hold a conversation.

'Well, this is fun,' shouts Rob in an effort to be heard above the noise.

'Fancy another game of Scrabble?' I ask.

'No not really. Anyhow, you always win.'

'Cards?'

'No, I think I'll just try and read my book,' says Rob, heading for the armchair.

The rain is relentless for the next three days. Rob has finished two books and even I'm sick of playing Scrabble. Then suddenly the sun appears. Unable to resist the fine weather we decide to spend the day sitting at the back of the house and enjoying the sun.

'If you let Patrick out he can have a hop around. We can keep an eye on him in case he starts eating the flowers again,' I call from the kitchen.

'Okay,' comes the reply from the yard.

Suddenly I hear Rob cry out.

'What's the matter love?' I ask, rushing outside to investigate.

'He just had a go at me. Tried to nip my hand.'

'Why? What did you do?'

'Nothing, absolutely nothing. I just reached out to stroke him but clearly he didn't like it.'

'That's odd. He's seemed a docile little thing. Maybe you startled him.'

'I don't think so, I approached him very slowly. Maybe he just doesn't like me.'

We grab a coffee and stand in the yard watching Patrick hop around the flower bed. Suddenly there's soil flying everywhere as he starts digging furiously. A couple of minutes later he's created a hollow in the flower-bed and plonks himself down, stretching his huge, furry feet out behind him.

'Maybe he just wants to cool off, it's a lot warmer today,' says Rob. 'At least he's not doing any damage.'

'I suppose not. Anyhow, are we going to go for a ride on the famous train? We can get off at the quarry and then walk back. It would do us good to have a stretch.'

'Okay. Are you going to put Flopsy Bunny in his hutch before we leave?'

'I guess we'd better, just in case he destroys the plants. I'll let you do it while I pop to the loo,' I say and walk back inside. As I shut the bathroom door there's an almighty cry from the yard. I rush outside to find Rob clutching his arm.

'Are you alright?'

'No I'm not, he just kicked me,' replies Rob.

'Kicked you?' I query in disbelief. 'How on earth did he manage to kick you Rob? He's tiny.'

'He ran at the wall then turned in mid-air and kicked out with his back legs. His feet caught me on the arm, look!'

And sure enough there are deep, scratch-marks on Rob's forearm.

'I wouldn't have believed it possible Rob. Maybe you're approaching him wrongly. Let me have a go.'

Gingerly I approach the little bundle of fluff and, sure enough, he's off again doing circuits of the yard, ricocheting off the high wall.

'Crikey! I wonder what all that's about?' I puzzle.

'Well he's not a happy bunny that's for sure.'

'Maybe we should risk leaving him out while we go for our walk. I mean he can't go anywhere can he? He might calm down if we leave him alone for a bit.'

'Well, if you're sure. I guess you're right. He certainly wouldn't be able to scale the wall.'

And so we head off to Braye Road to board the famous Alderney train. Three hours later we're home again.

'Well, that was exciting!' says Rob sarcastically. 'Good grief, it doesn't even go anywhere Chris. What's the point of going two miles across the island to end up in a disused quarry?'

Clearly our excursion hasn't excited my husband.

'My brother would have loved that! It's one of the British Isles' first railways. Queen Victoria rode on it when she visited.'

'That may be the case but sitting in an old London tube carriage looking at a hedge really didn't do it for me Chris.

There was no view and there wasn't even anything at the end of the line except that abandoned quarry. How that can be a major tourist attraction beats me. Let's face it, there's nothing to do here unless you like walking or playing golf.'

'Oh stop whinging, I actually like it here. I'm going to go and see what Patrick's been up to. Hopefully he hasn't demolished the flower-bed.'

However, it's worse than that. Patrick is nowhere to be seen and in the middle of the flower-bed is a very large pile of earth. I climb up onto the dwarf wall and to my horror can see a large burrow that disappears under the foundations of the downstairs bathroom.

'Rooooooob!' I shout.

Rob appears quickly, obviously worried that I've been injured.

'Darling, are you alright? What have you done?'

'I haven't done anything but Patrick has. Come and have a look at this.'

Rob joins me on top of the retaining wall and looks in disbelief at the huge pile of earth and the beginnings of the tunnel.

'Good grief! What on earth's he done?'

'Well it's a bit obvious isn't it? He's decided to dig a burrow.'

'But how are we going to get him out? He must have gone a heck of a way under the foundations,' says Rob, crouching down to get a better look at the excavations. 'I'll go and see if I can find a torch so that we can see how far he's gone.'

A few minutes later Rob returns with a large lantern torch, lies down on the ground and shines it down the hole.

'He must be at least ten feet down. I can just see his eyes. How on earth did such a tiny creature manage to shift so much earth? He must have been working like fury while we were out.'

'You're telling me! And look at this,' I say, having caught sight of the inside of Patrick's hutch. 'He's totally shredded all the newspaper and it looks as though he's taken some of the hay with him unless he managed to eat it all before he started burrowing.'

'What weird behaviour! Maybe we can tempt him out with a carrot. He likes carrots.'

Two hours later there's still no sign of Patrick and the mound of goodies to tempt him out has grown dramatically. Besides carrots there are apples, cabbage leaves and dandelions but nothing seems tasty enough to lure him out.

'Well there's not much we can do except make sure that he has food and water. I'll go and put the kettle on, I could do with a cuppa after all the excitement.'

As we sit over our tea, battling with a crossword, the phone rings.

'Shall I answer it?' asks Rob.

'I suppose so, it might be Alan and Marie.'

As he reaches for the phone I suddenly shout,

'No don't! What are we going to tell them? Gosh Rob. We need to think this one through.'

For the next half hour we consider the options. We don't want to alarm our hosts and spoil their holiday, but at the same time we need to prepare them for what might greet them on their return.

'Okay. How's about, we're sorry to trouble you, but Patrick has dug a tunnel under the house and is refusing to come out. Do you have any suggestions as to how to retrieve him?' says Rob, poker-faced.

'Rob, this isn't a laughing matter. I really don't see how we're going to coax him out.'

'What about a broom?'

'That'll simply push him in further and frighten him.'

'Okay then what about using the hoover? We could suck him out!'

'Oh Rob, please stop being stupid. You always do this.

Whenever things are serious you go into silly mode. I think we're just going to have to sit this out and let him emerge in his own good time.'

Two days later there's still no sign of our charge, although some of the food has disappeared and there's evidence of rabbit-droppings on the ground.

'Well at least it's proof that he's eating and that he's still alive,' I say assuredly.

'I'm sure it'll have a satisfactory ending,' says Rob. 'He might unearth some more Roman remains while he's under there. That would keep the museum happy. A stash of gold coins or the odd amphora. I can see it now in the local paper, "Attila the Bun unearths lost neolithic settlement." '

I glare at him and go out to see if there's any more sign of activity. Just as I'm about to step out of the door, who should come tentatively peeping out of his tunnel but Patrick. Except he looks a bit strange. He's got a wild look about him and his fur seems to have grown around his neck like a ruff. I keep very still in case I startle him and watch as he sits up on his back legs and starts to pull the fur out from around his neck. Unfortunately he's already sensed my presence and, with a loud thump of his hind leg, disappears back into the darkness. I go back indoors to give Rob my progress report.

'Well, that was weird.'

'What was?'

'Well, he did show up for a moment and started pulling the fur out of his neck but he's scooted back into his burrow. I think I'll have a look online and see what Google has to say. I'm sure other people must have experienced this sort of thing before.'

And so I pose the question, 'Why is my rabbit pulling fur out of his neck?'

'Well?' asks Rob looking over my shoulder. 'What's the verdict?'

'I'm confused. Hang on and I'll read it to you. "A common

reason for fur pulling is the instinct to make a nest. When a rabbit is preparing for kits, her body secretes hormones that cause the fur on her sides & belly to loosen. ... Unspayed females who live with no other rabbits or only other females can experience false pregnancies.'"

'Well that's all very well but that's referring to female rabbits not fellas,' says Rob.

'Mmmm. True. Maybe he's got mites or a skin complaint of some sort. Perhaps we should take him to the vet.'

'First catch your rabbit,' says Rob.

'Oh grief, of course. Stupid me. And we can hardly expect the vet to fly over just to come and peer down a hole at a manic rabbit. This is a messy one Rob.'

It's late that night while we're lying in bed trying to get to sleep that it hits me.

'Rob!'

'What?' replies a sleepy voice.

'I think I've solved it!'

'Which one? 3 down or 15 across?'

'Ha ha. Neither Mr Funny. It's Patrick. He isn't a buck, he's a doe! It's all adding up. The fact that he became aggressive and then dug a burrow and now he's pulling his fur out. He thinks he's pregnant!'

At this Rob sits up and puts the light back on.

'You mean they got the sex wrong?'

'Precisely! Thumper had a pseudopregnancy a couple of times before I had her spayed. She used to shred her bedding and then use it to make a nest, then she'd line it with her fur. Patrick thinks he's going to have baby bunnies!'

'In which case we'd better re-name him!' laughs Rob.

And so the next day we watch carefully as Patricia ventures out into the open seeking food. Sure enough she's looking like an old sofa with the stuffing coming out. As she turns tail I catch a glimpse of her teats, swollen and ready to produce milk.

'Oh poor thing. You've got to feel sorry for her. All this palaver and no babies at the end of it all. It's a shame.'

'But how long does one of these phantom things last?' asks Rob.

'Anything between sixteen to eighteen days apparently.'

'And how long have we been here?'

'Mmm, let's see. This'll be day twelve so they're going to be back before she's through all this.'

'So not only has Patrick dug a tunnel under the foundations of their house but he's had a sex-change in their absence. This is going to go down well Chris!'

Even I have to laugh.

'We'll just have to be up front darling, it isn't anything that we can hide from them, it'll just be a bit of a shock. Patricia'll be fine once she gets through this and then they can fill the tunnel in.'

'I must admit I'll be glad to get home Chris,' confesses Rob. 'I mean it isn't the most thrilling of places. I think I'd go stir-crazy if I lived here and this sit hasn't exactly been very exciting has it?'

'Excuse me! Who was the one who said that rabbits were boring?' I remind him.

Three days later and we're busy packing our bags ready to head for the airport the next morning.

'I guess you'd better give Alan a ring and explain what's happened Rob. I mean we don't want them to come home and think a JCB has crashed through the wall.'

'I'd better ring? Why me? I think it would be better if you ring Marie. Women are more understanding of these things.'

For once I back down and agree.

'Well? Was she okay about it all?' asks Rob as I return from the sitting-room.

'Yes, very understanding and grateful actually, although I think the gender fluidity came as a bit of a shock. However, I'm afraid they've got some bad news.'

'Oh? What's happened? Nothing serious I hope?'

'Well it hasn't actually happened yet but I don't think you're going to like this.'

'Stop being cryptic Chris and get to the point,' says Rob becoming irritated.

'They're anticipating being stuck in Southampton. The forecast's for thick fog for the next three days and it's heading our way too. I'm afraid we won't be going anywhere for a while.'

A loud groan echoes throughout the kitchen as Rob crashes his head down on the table.

'Fancy a game of Scrabble?' I ask.

# 11

## THE GOOD LIFE

'I DON'T THINK IT WOULD hurt us to be a bit more ambitious Rob,' I suggest one evening while perusing the internet for another house-sit.

A rural small-holding sounded idyllic.

'I mean we managed the pigs in Wales without too much trouble. I can't imagine that a few sheep would be much of a problem. As for a horse I'd love that. I used to ride when I was young, in fact I always dreamed of having my own pony.'

'I don't want anything to do with horses,' replies Rob quickly. 'I got thrown off one once and ended up with concussion. I'd be quite happy never to go near one again. They have teeth and hooves and they kick. If you want to apply for this farm sit then fair enough but I'm not going to get involved with anything except dogs and cats. Anyhow, where is it? Somewhere remote no doubt.'

'No, it's near Evesham, so not far from civilisation and we could get to Worcester quite easily. You'd be alright with sheep wouldn't you? All you'd need to do is make sure they'd got food and water and that they weren't lame or maggoty or anything.'

'No Chris. I am not going to get involved with the farm side of things. If you want to play at being what's-her-name, Barbara, in The Good Life that's fine, but I am not going to play Tom.'

And at that Rob walks out of the kitchen and heads for bed.

'So this is Nell,' says Ernie, patting the head of a handsome black and white sheep-dog that's following us along the farm track. 'She's a good worker and very obedient, aren't you gal? But mind you, if she were a sheep I wouldn't buy 'er at market, she's getting a bit long in the tooth now, aren't you lass?'

Nell looks up at him, ears cocked, and wags her tail furiously, pleased by the attention. At the same time I can't help noticing that Ernie has no teeth at all, or maybe he's just forgotten to put them in this morning. He somehow seems to squeeze his words out from between his gums but at times it's quite difficult to make out what he's saying.

'You won't need 'er to work the sheep as they're all grazing on top of the common now that lambing's over. 'Er can always help you if they stray too far but 'er knows what to do, don't you gal? You'll just need to check the water troughs are topped up if this dry spell continues. I've left a couple of plastic barrels up there for you. Any problems and our neighbour Alf Davies'll give you a hand. I've warned 'im you're comin' and I've left you 'is number by the phone along with the vet's. Now, are you sure you're comfortable with the horse lass?' he asks. 'She hasn't bin ridden for a long while.'

'Oh yes, that'll be a treat for me,' I reply. 'Is she a quiet ride?'

'Ha! She was retired from Riding for the Disabled so she's bomb-proof is old Judy. She'll enjoy a gentle walk round the common with you. But mind you she has a funny way of walkin'. She tends to crab. You'll see what I mean when you take 'er out. All her kit's in the barn next to the house along with her food.'

I'm in seventh heaven, my own pony is a childhood dream come true.

'Now Rambeau, he's a different kettle of fish,' he continues.

'Rambeau?' I ask.

'He's our tup and a good one too, he covered the whole flock this year, but to be truthful 'e's a nasty bugga. My advice would be to stay away from 'im. You can fill the water trough from the tap without goin' in 'is field and feed 'im from 'is bucket. Bad tempered devil 'e is. Sent me flying a couple of times and the missus! Once 'e's done with the ewes I keep 'im out o' the way.'

I try not to let my face give away my now quite serious

concern and am beginning to feel relieved that I've left Rob behind at the house to unload the car.

'So where are you off to then Ernie? Somewhere nice?' I ask.

'Yes, we're off to Madeira again for a bit o' warm weather. We've been goin' there for the last fifteen years. The missus likes to get away this time o' year once we've finished lambing. Between you and me she's not too good these days. Touch of that dementia thing so 'er memory isn't what it used to be. It's beginning to cause problems, but not much we can do about that. Anyhow, I've told the doctor I'm not 'avin 'er goin' into any home. This is where she was born and this is where she'll die.'

He leans on his stick and looks out over the land, suddenly overcome with emotion. I find my own eyes tearing up and am glad when he returns to business.

'Now, I need to show you the calves, we've got two at the moment. We don't normally have calves but the farm next door had a cow that had twins. Difficult birth and the old lady rejected 'em. Alf felt they were too much trouble cos they have to be bottle fed, so Dora took 'em on. I'll have to show you the formula and the measures. One of 'em's a greedy fella so you'll need to make sure 'e doesn't guzzle or 'e'll get all gassy and then you will 'av a problem. Come on and I'll show you where everything is.'

As we walk back down the track to the barn I'm beginning to get quietly worried about the responsibility. A vicious ram and a guzzling calf. Still, this was what I'd wanted and now was my chance to prove that I could manage everything.

We round the corner to the barn where I notice a very small lady in a flowery dress with grey hair swept back in an untidy bun. She's standing staring at the calves and doesn't seem to have noticed us arrive.

'Dora, this is Christine,' shouts Ernie.

Dora looks round but her face doesn't show any expression. She shuffles over to me and gapes at me blankly.

'Should I know you?' she asks, staring up into my face.

'No Dora. I'm Christine. I've come to help out with the animals while you're on holiday. It's nice to meet you,' I smile.

'Holiday? Am I going on holiday?' she asks turning round and looking quizzically at Ernie.

'Yes love, you know you are, we're going to Madeira.'

'Oh that'll be nice. I've never been to Madeira,' she replies and a gentle smile spreads across her face.

'Do you like magazines?' she asks.

I'm bemused by the rather bizarre question.

'Yes, Dora, I do.'

'Good,' she replies. 'I like magazines.'

As she turns and totters back to the house I feel suddenly overwhelmed by the sadness of her condition. She seems so childlike and innocent and I can't help but wonder how Ernie's going to cope with a journey to Madeira.


A few days later, Ernie and Dora departed, I'm beginning to get into the rhythm of the work. Rob is staying well out of the way although he is keeping to his word in looking after Nell and the farmyard cats. We're neither of us used to having such an obedient dog and she's a pleasure to have around.

'Do you know she won't even go through a door or a gate before me,' remarks Rob one morning. 'She always waits and her recall is incredible. It must be a joy to work a flock of sheep with a dog like this.'

'Er, excuse me,' I reply. 'May I remind you that you wanted nothing to do with the farm animals so just keep your dog away from my sheep Mr Drabble!'

'Mr Drabble? Who's Mr Drabble?'

'Don't you remember him? Phil Drabble. He used to have a programme on TV called 'One Man and his Dog'. They used to feature sheep-dog trials. I used to love to watch it.'

'No. Must have been before my time,' says Rob, smirking.

After lunch I head for the barn to tack up Judy. She's already waiting at the gate and whinnies as I approach. I pop the halter on her head and lead her out into the yard. I give her coat a good brush down and smile as she shivers every time I move the brush over her withers. I can't resist nuzzling into her soft nose as I just love the smell of her and the soft, velvety feel of her muzzle. Memories from childhood come flooding back from the smell alone. She waits patiently while I struggle with her bridle but, once I've got the bit in her mouth, the rest is straightforward. I throw the saddle over her back, tighten the girth and lead her over to a bale of hay which proves a good mounting block and, after adjusting the stirrups, I'm soon on board. With a gentle squeeze of my legs and a 'walk on' she lumbers off and we head for the common.

It's bliss. Absolute bliss. The air is warm and the views are simply amazing. We climb the hill where the wood, which cradles one side of the farm in the crook of its arm, gives way to open countryside, and we can see for miles. Below us the Avon threads its course through the patchwork of market gardens and the Malverns rise proudly in the distance. As we amble along in first gear I decide to try a gentle trot but hold onto the pommel of the saddle for reassurance, not having been on the back of a horse for years. I soon get into the rhythm but when I look up I begin to understand what Ernie means about crabbing. Judy is actually moving across the common on the diagonal, which, if we were in a dressage class might win us a few points. However, as the main purpose of our outing is to check on the sheep, I have to work out how to steer her around the perimeter of the common, which involves a modicum of mathematical calculation. I walk Judy slowly round the flock that all seem to be in good order, but I'm beginning to wish that I'd paid more attention in geometry as I attempt to work out how to get us back to the track that led up onto the common.

It's at this point that three large, black horses come galloping towards us, seemingly having arrived out of nowhere. They're big and strong and horribly curious. They skid to a halt when they reach us but surround us in a menacing way, heads rearing and tails thrashing. Judy is wonderful and remains unperturbed, but my heart is racing and I really don't know how to deal with this. Stay in the saddle and hope they'll go away or dismount in an attempt to shoo them off and risk getting crushed or trampled on? I'm actually shaking and have no idea how to handle the horrible situation.

Suddenly, and to my huge relief, a grey horse appears in the distance and it's got someone in the saddle. Horse and rider come cantering over to us and a rather handsome man calls out,

'You okay?'

'No, not really. I've had rather a nasty fright.'

'Stay put and I'll get rid of them,' he shouts.

And, as I sit tight on Judy, my rescuer skilfully rides up and puts himself and his horse between us and the offending trio. With the deft use of his crop on their hind quarters he persuades the horses to move away and I heave a sigh of relief as they canter noisily off into the distance.

'Oh thank you so much. I was a bit shaken up,' I confess.

'You're not the first person to be ambushed,' he replies. 'We've all complained to the owners about those three being grazed up here. They're bordering on being dangerous. I'm just pleased I was able to help. I'm Jeff by the way.'

'Christine,' I say, leaning out of the saddle to shake his hand.

He really is a handsome chap and every inch the country gent. His tweed cap sits jauntily on a head of silver-grey hair and he smiles warmly at me.

'Where were you heading?' he asks.

'I was just doing the rounds to check the sheep were okay. My husband and I are looking after the farm while the Faulkners are away. I was just about to head back to the house.'

'Well, let me keep you company, just so that I know you've got back safely.'

I explain Judy's peculiarity of crabbing which makes him chuckle and I find myself blushing.

'Well, it makes for an interesting ride I suppose,' he laughs. 'So are you enjoying being a farmer's wife?'

'Do you know, I'm loving it. It feels so invigorating and I love the rhythm of the day. I'm beginning to wish I'd chosen this way of life. It knocks spots off being in an office.'

'Worcestershire's a beautiful part of the country that's for sure,' he replies, 'and there's nothing better than enjoying it from the back of a horse.'

As we reach the end of the track I quietly find myself wishing it was longer.

'Well, I'll say my goodbye. It might be safer to take a vehicle up there if you need to do another inspection. We wouldn't want you getting hurt.'

'I can't thank you enough,' I reply.

And at that he waves goodbye and canters off across the common. I turn Judy's head and calculate the line of attack in order to get us back to the farmhouse.

When I get back to the yard, Rob's sitting in the garden with Nell dozing at his feet. I soon realise that Rob's dozing too, his head tilted back in his chair, mouth open. As I slide down from the saddle he stirs and looks up sleepily.

'Oh, hello darling. Did you enjoy your ride?'

'Yes, until we got rounded up by a posse of wild horses. It was like that advert for Lloyd's Bank when a load of stallions come charging along the beach. But we're okay thanks. Mr D'Arcy rescued us,' and a broad smile suddenly spreads across my face as I lead Judy back to her field.

'I meant to mention,' mumbles Rob between mouthfuls at breakfast the following morning. 'We ran out of loo roll yesterday while you were out so I thought I'd better have a search in the bathroom cupboard.'

'Mmm. And?'

'Well, I don't think we'll be running short while we're here. There must be over a hundred in there.'

'A hundred? Isn't that a bit of an exaggeration?'

'No, really. Come and look,' replies Rob, taking me by the hand and leading me upstairs to the bathroom.

'There!' he says, opening the cupboard door.

'Good grief!' I exclaim. 'You're right!' In fact Rob has probably underestimated the quantity.

'But why?' he asks.

'Maybe they just hoard things in case they get snowed in, but it does seem to be an inordinately big stash. Bizarre. Anyhow, I must go and see the calves and the tup, I'm already late for their morning feed and Rambeau'll be complaining soon.'

Sure enough, as I head towards his field I can hear the clanging of metal as he butts the metal rungs of the gate with his horns, a sure indication that he's getting impatient, not having been given his grub.

'Here you are then big fella,' I say as I approach the gate. Unfortunately his bucket has managed to stray away from the gate but, after listening to Ernie's warning, I don't feel inclined to go and retrieve it while his lordship is standing there. I manage to grab an old broom that's lying on the ground and use it to work the bucket over to the gate, slip my hand through the bars, grab the handle and stand it upright. The moment I start to pour the sheep nuts out of the sack Rambeau sticks his head in the way and the feed showers all over his back and onto the ground. He doesn't seem too worried and is soon scoffing his breakfast. I reach through the bars and give his woolly head a scratch. It feels solid, coarse and oily but he doesn't seem to object.

Leaving him munching happily I head off to feed the

calves. This is a more complicated task as it involves the careful measuring of the formula feed into their bottles, however I love the excitement that follows when I walk into the barn and two little black and white faces poke out through the bars, eyes rolling and tongues stretched out in anticipation. I've become more adept at feeding them now and am amazed at just how quickly they can empty a bottle. According to one of the websites that I've been looking at a calf can drink a pint in a minute, but little Guzzle-guts can drink even faster than that and I have to give him breathers from the teat to stop him downing it all too quickly. Job done I head back to the house where Rob is doing the washing-up.

'Everything okay?' he asks.

'Yes, all good thanks. Rambeau's a happy boy and the babies have had their bottles. What about you?'

'I'm fine but I've had another interesting discovery.'

'Mm, what's that?'

'Marmalade,' replies Rob.

'Marmalade? What do you mean marmalade?'

Rob walks over to the door of the pantry and, with a flourish, opens it to reveal shelves full of jars of shop-bought marmalade.

'Ta-dah!'

'Good grief! This is like the loo rolls Rob, it's really odd. Do you know, I reckon it must have something to do with Dora's dementia. I guess she's buying stuff because she's forgotten she's already got it.'

'Oh golly I never thought of that. I guess you're right. How sad. I hope we don't end up losing our marbles.'

'No, we'd end up with a cupboard full of marmite and Lindt chocolate bars,' I laugh and head out to see my horse.

It's the next morning when things go horribly wrong. I head out to the barn with my two bottles of milk for the twins, thinking how wonderful it is to have so many animals and to be enjoying the countryside in such a hands-on way. As the babies suck I suddenly realise that I've lost concentration and, to my horror, little Guzzle-guts has drunk his milk in record time and is trying to wrap his mouth round his brother's bottle. Exactly what I'm supposed to prevent. I'm praying that all will be well but realise I'd better hang on for a while to make sure that my baby is okay. He isn't. After a few minutes he starts crying, gives a loud moan and falls to the ground, eyes rolling. I've only read about it but can only imagine that this is colic and realise that I need to act swiftly.

'Rob! Rob!' I cry out. 'Quickly, I need your help!'

For once Rob has actually heard me first time and is already running into the barn.

'Quick, I need to get this baby into the Landrover. I think he's got colic. I've got to get him to the vet's quickly.'

Fortunately the vehicle is already close by but lifting a calf, especially one that's in pain, is an incredibly tricky business.

'We'll have to heave him up into the back. I'll grab some straw so that he's not lying on the bed of the vehicle. Oh heavens, this is exactly what I was supposed to prevent. What if he dies?'

'He won't die, come on. It wasn't your fault Chris,' say Rob encouragingly but I feel wretched.

A clumsy, joint effort sees my baby safely into the back of the Landrover.

'I'd better come with you,' says Rob.

'No, don't worry. By the time we've locked everything up we'll have wasted time. I'll just hit the road.'

'Have you got your phone on you?'

'Yes, and before you ask, it's switched on. I'll ring you when I get to the vet's. I'm pretty sure I know where it is. I'll shout if there's a problem.'

As I start up the engine my heart's racing. How am I going to explain a dead calf to Ernie? I try to drive carefully down the track to the main road but it's full of potholes and the calf is moaning and bleating in the back. The bumps can't be helping his swollen tummy, poor thing. We bounce from one side of the track to the other and at one point my head hits the roof of the cab as we drive over a huge boulder and crash down into a rut. Suddenly there's a very loud noise akin to someone letting the air out of a balloon. The smell that accompanies it is foul, but I am grinning from ear to ear. I can see in the rear view mirror that the patient is trying to scramble to his feet. I stop the vehicle and turn round to see Guzzle-guts looking at me with an expression that can only be described as relief, but it couldn't be as big as the relief that I feel. It seems that the built-up gas has managed to escape and that my little fella is actually okay. I execute a five-point turn and drive gingerly back towards the farmhouse, eager to share the good news with Rob. As we pull up in the farm-yard I call out to him but there's no reply.

'Rob. Rob?'

There's still no reply so I go into the house. Maybe he's popped to the loo.

'Rob? Are you there?'

A groan seems to be coming from the direction of the upper floor so I start climbing the stairs.

'Darling, are you there?'

'I'm in here,' cries a weak voice from the bedroom.

I open the door to find Rob flat out on the bed.

'You're back quickly, is everything alright?' he asks pathetically.

'Yes, I know, and everything's fine, but why are you lying down love? Aren't you feeling well?'

'No. Just after you left I heard a clanging sound coming from Rambeau's field so I went down to investigate.'

'And?'

'He'd got his head trapped between the bars on the gate. One of his horns was well and truly caught and he was butting so furiously that the gate was crashing backwards and forwards. I reckoned that either he was going to pull it off its hinges or his head off his neck.'

'So what did you do?'

'Well I tried to free him from this side of the gate but I couldn't shift him so I decided I was going to have to risk going in the field with him.'

I hold my head in my hands, not wanting to know the rest of this story.

'I knew that if I managed to free him I was going to have to get out of his way quickly. I got him to turn his head sideways and his horn came back through the gate, so at that point I headed for the fence with the intention of vaulting over it, before he had the chance to attack me.'

'But?'

'I didn't quite make it, so I ended up falling over the fence and landing on my side. I think I'm just badly bruised but I might have broken a rib something Chris. I'm in a lot of pain.'

Two hours and a couple of whiskies later, my beloved seems to be on the road to recovery with no broken bones.

'So much for the good life!' I laugh. 'At least Guzzle-guts didn't die and I didn't fall off Judy.'

'No, and I've loved being with Nell. She's such a sweetheart, I'll really miss her. I like being doted on.'

'I'll obviously have to try harder in future,' I smile.

The next morning we make sure that all is well with the animals and that the house is in good order before Ernie and Dora return. Nell's ears suddenly prick up and, with an excited bark, she runs off down the track where we can see Ernie's car bumping along towards the farm, her tail wagging furiously. As they pull into the yard she's beside herself with excitement. Ernie climbs out of the car looking tanned and relaxed and she hurls herself at him, tail wagging, paws on his chest, and covers him with kisses.

''Av you missed me then lass?' Ernie asks her. ''Av they looked after you then? I hope you've bin no trouble,' he says looking in our direction and smiling.

Dora appears from round the side of the car looking ruddy and healthy.

'Hello Dora,' I say.

'Should I know you?' she replies looking at me suspiciously.

'It's Christine. We've been looking after the animals for you while you were away. Did you have a nice holiday?'

'Holiday? Have I been on holiday?' Dora asks, looking at Ernie with a confused expression, then back at me. 'Do you like magazines?' she asks.

# 12

## RAINING CATS AND DOGS

HECTOR IS LYING QUIETLY on the kitchen floor. A handsome, pedigree doberman, sired by a Cruft's champion. He's a strong, dignified-looking animal with an intelligent head and a powerful body but he's also one of the soppiest dogs we have yet to meet.

His owners, Margaret and Phil, took Hector on as a rescue dog from a family in Yorkshire who'd decided to part with him following several bouts of sheep-worrying. The family had done everything they could to stop him, trying out all manner of things to deter him, terrified that he could be shot at any time by a local farmer if caught in the act. Sadly none of the tried and tested methods proved effective and Hector's behaviour showed that he still had a thirst for chasing sheep. Confined to a pen with a ram for several days resulted in no more than a staring match and dear Hector returned home, his behaviour unchanged. Broken-hearted to have to part with their beloved boy, the family decided to try to rehome him. That was when Margaret and Phil stepped in, keen to have a dog that could act as a watch-dog. Having been recently burgled, reinsurance was proving a costly business because, according to the insurance companies, statistically, once a home has been burgled, it's very likely to be targeted a second time.

One company had suggested that a policy would be less costly if Margaret and Phil got themselves a guard-dog so, after much discussion, they agreed that a doberman would be the ideal choice. A search online brought Hector's plight to their attention and, having fallen for his good looks, they contacted his owners. It was agreed that a home in Cornwall would be an ideal place for him to live as he could run freely on the many beaches and be safely out of contact with any wooly temptation, Cornwall being fundamentally cattle country.

It was a match made in heaven and once Hector had settled in and got to know his new family the three of them had enjoyed many holidays together. However, for the first time, teachers Margaret and Phil, have decided to leave him at home while they go away for a well-earned half-term break. It seems that their last holiday with Hector in tow had turned into a bit of a disaster, making them hugely reluctant to risk another incident.

'It happened while we were on holiday in the Lake District,' recounts Phil, as we sit outside in the garden enjoying a beer. 'We'd deliberately chosen an area where there were no sheep so that we didn't have to worry about Hector. He loved it, didn't he Margaret? He was covering a heck of a lot of ground while we stumbled up the fells panting. It was tough going at times but he was amazing, until one day we noticed that he was limping.'

'Yes,' continues Margaret. 'He'd cut his pad really badly and we had an awful job getting him back down Cat Bells to the car. He couldn't really walk and, needless to say, he's not very easy to carry. We took him straight to the vet who gave us some anti-inflammatories and said that we shouldn't walk the old fella for a few days.'

'Cost us a fortune I can tell you, and our holiday scuppered to boot!' recalls Phil. 'We didn't dare leave him in the holiday cottage while we went out walking, so we decided we'd do some of the local National Trust properties instead, as we could leave him in the car for an hour. Not really our sort of thing but at least it was something to do. It was while we were walking through the grand hall of this country pile, admiring the portraits and all that, that a curator came rushing in. He seemed to be in quite a flap. He asked if anyone in the room owned a red Citroen CV and read out a registration number. Well, I suddenly realised to my horror that it was ours!'

The look in Phil's eyes suggests that the memory is still very raw.

'Well, I called out that yes, it was ours and was there a problem? Needless to say my mind was in overdrive thinking that the alarm was probably going off thanks to Hector. But it was worse than that, much worse.'

Phil takes a swig of beer from his glass and continues.

'The guy said he was afraid there'd been a terrible accident. Our car had rolled backwards down the hill in the car park. An old lady standing behind it saw someone in the driving seat and assumed it was a person, but of course it was Hector. She obviously thought that the car would stop and only just got out of the way in time. Apparently it very nearly ran her over and she was in shock.'

'I was obviously concerned about the old lady,' interrupts Margaret, 'so I suggested that we'd better go and see if she was alright. We reckoned Hector must have knocked the hand-break off.'

'But it didn't stop there!' exclaims Phil, 'it got worse! The car had continued to roll down the hill and crashed into the side of a coach. There was an awful lot of damage. What with the car out of action and a lame dog it cost us a fortune to get home. Result? No more walking holidays for Hector I'm afraid.'

At the sound of his name and the 'w' word, Hector pricks up his ears but, recognising that no-one is making a move, quickly puts his head back down and sighs.

'I'm afraid he needs loads of exercise. He runs like the wind but he's beautiful to watch. I just hope he doesn't prove too much for you, it's so kind of you to take him on,' says Margaret looking at us apologetically. 'But he's an absolute sweetheart and, if truth be known, a bit of a wimp!'

'Don't worry,' reassures Rob, 'I'm sure we'll be fine.'

Hector's energy is, indeed, relentless. We walk him on the nearby beach at Polzeith and, after a day on the lead and practising his recall, decide to risk letting him run free. He has a majestic air and we marvel at the fluidity of his action.

'You can see the champion in him,' remarks Rob. 'He's a delight to watch when he runs, isn't he?'

Fortunately Hector seems an obedient fellow, providing there's a treat at the end of the recall. He's surprisingly nervous of other dogs and returns quickly to our sides if there's even a hint of conflict. If a pack of dogs comes sniffing round him he's very quick to seek our protection.

It's after a few days of keeping Hector in our company that we feel comfortable enough leaving him for a couple of hours while we venture out to explore. He protests a little when he realises that we're going out without him, but settles down on his bed with a chew having been reassured that we'll be back before too long. We leave the house after breakfast and return a little more than an hour later, laden with provisions for our stay.

On opening the front door we're immediately aware of a fine, white cloud that has settled over the entire hallway. Initially we're unsure what the 'cloud' consists of but, on closer examination, realise that it's the padding from a large jiffy-bag that's been torn apart in our absence. The postman's obviously delivered a parcel which has proved too much of a temptation for Hector who's torn it apart to examine the contents.

Two hours later we're still attempting to hoover up the evidence. The fine, paper pulp from inside the bag is clinging to every possible surface and whatever it was that was in the bag has been shredded. In fact it's difficult to know what the contents might once have been.

'We're just going to have to leave him in the conservatory the next time we go out Rob. We can't risk him eating any more of the post,' I sigh.

Although we explore all the nearby beaches, Polzeith remains our favourite and Hector loves it. He likes to explore the rock-pools but isn't too keen on going in the sea. The breakers here are quite intimidating unless you're a surfer, so the pools offer an ideal way of cooling off. He wades around and occasionally lies down, enjoying the salt water.

After a few days of walking the beach we've got to know some of the other dog-walkers. Needless to say we know the names of the dogs not their owners. There's Stan the standard poodle, another rescue, a beautiful flatcoat retriever called Becky who likes to retrieve stones from the rock-pools, a glamorous saluki whose name is unpronounceable and therefore ultimately forgettable, and a yappy little Yorkie called Kimmy. No introductions are needed when you have a dog, they're the common ground around which conversation revolves.

It's one morning on the beach when we're on our way back to the car that we bump into Kimmy's owner and stop for a chat. It's a windy day and the surf has attracted a big crowd. It's a fascinating culture which attracts people of all ages, especially, I've noted, those who are getting on a bit. We're deep in conversation when suddenly a very shaggy mutt, covered in wet sand, appears from nowhere, bounds over to Rob, lifts his leg and pees all down his new jeans. I see the look of abject horror spread across Rob's face but can't help collapsing into fits of laughter. Hector comes running over to inspect and have a good sniff and I'm half expecting him to lift his leg too in order to confirm ownership of Rob's leg.

'What the hell was that about?' he cries, clearly furious at having been used as a lamppost and, at the same time, looking around for the owner. 'And I don't know what you're finding so funny,' he shouts, looking furiously in my direction. 'It's disgusting. People should have more control over their dogs. Fancy letting your animal go round peeing on people. Whoever owns him had better watch out, I'm warning you Chris!'

I keep trying not to laugh but it does still seem incredibly funny and the more I laugh the angrier Rob becomes.

'It's alright for you standing there laughing. Not only have

I got a wet leg but it's going to ruin my jeans and my shoe. I'm going to walk back up the beach to the shower and try to wash all this off.'

And with that Rob stomps off towards the toilet block, foot squelching in his shoe.

As I watch him make his way back up the beach I can't help but notice a rather curvaceous blonde running frantically towards him. She's wearing a wet suit and has clearly been surfing as her long, wet hair is draped back from her face. I'm reminded of Ursula Andress emerging from the sea in 'Dr No' but fortunately more fully clad. She manages to stop Rob in his tracks and is gesticulating wildly and holding her head in her hands. I quicken my pace and head in their direction, Hector at my heels.

'No, of course not,' I overhear Rob saying as I approach. 'Oh, don't worry, these things happen. It's nothing that a drop of water won't sort out. He's a lovely dog, a very handsome fellow. No, really don't worry, it's fine, they're just an old pair of jeans, it'll wash out.'

At this point Ursula Andress slinks off along the sand with her shaggy mutt by her side, then turns round smiling and waves, leaving Rob staring longingly after her. Hector is now by his side, tongue lolling and I can't help noticing the similarity.

I fold my arms and find my lip curling upwards slightly at one side.

'You seem to have forgiven old shaggy bonce then?' I remark sarcastically.

'Apparently it's just what he does. She was hugely apologetic and very embarrassed. It would have been difficult to be angry with her.'

'I'm sure it would darling. What man would want to argue with an attractive, rubber-clad blonde?'

A shrug of the shoulders and my man heads for the showers with a big grin on his face.

The next day, wanting to visit Land's End before our sit finishes, we decide to leave Hector at home, but safely contained in the conservatory so that he doesn't get the chance to eat any more of the post. I move his bed through from the kitchen and settle him down with Tigger, one of his favourite toys.

'Back soon Hector. You be a good boy!' I say, dropping a couple of treats onto his bed.

Land's End turns out to be an expensive tourist trap and so, without even paying the extortionate fee to park the car, we do a u-turn and head for home. The sky is a seriously dark, gun-metal grey and it's clearly going to pour down. The rain starts almost immediately, huge drops that sound more like hail-stones when they hit the roof of the car.

'Yuk! I'm glad we didn't stop, we'd have got soaked,' I remark.

'Mmm. This is going to get serious,' replies Rob glancing up at the sky. 'We'd best just head for home, there's no point in staying out in this.'

The rain is coming down so hard that the wind-screen wipers can't work fast enough and visibility is a real problem. Suddenly there's a loud bang and the sky lights up as a flash of lightning appears momentarily ahead of us, silhouetting the church tower of St Endellion.

'Jeepers! That was close,' shouts Rob above the noise of the downpour.

He has to drive slowly as the narrow, Cornish lanes are awash and already flooding in places. Another loud boom is quickly followed by an even more dramatic flash of lightning.

'We'd better get home to Hector. He'll be frightened by all this, poor chap.'

As Rob pulls the car up into the drive we make a hasty dash for the front door. It's raining so heavily that we're soaked to the skin in just the short time that it takes us to get into the house.

As I head through to the conservatory I can hear whimpering and, on opening the door, find a quivering Hector cowering on the floor with his head thrust under one of the seat cushions of the settee. Or should I say what is left of the settee. He's obviously been so terrified that he's chewed the entire sofa and there's no part of it undamaged. The room is carpeted in small pieces of foam, Hector having destroyed all the seat and back cushions in his agitated state. The wood of the legs and arms are covered with bite-marks and there's a large puddle on the tiled floor that is leeching into the carpet.

'Yikes!' exclaims Rob.

'It's a lot worse than yikes,' I reply, heading over to comfort poor Hector. 'This is going to be an insurance claim if ever there was one.'

'That should go down well with the insurance company!' he laughs.

Then the laugh gets louder and Rob begins to snort.

'Okay, it wasn't that funny,' I reply, 'and goodness knows what Margaret and Phil will think.'

'Yes, but at least it's a bona fido claim,' replies Rob heading for the hall cupboard to get the hoover.

# 13

# GOOGLE

'I DIDN'T MENTION IT last night because you were too tired, but I've applied for another sit,' I announce to Rob one morning over breakfast.

I've learned to choose my moments carefully and breakfast has proved to be the best time to slip things in gently, between mouthfuls of muesli and a strong cup of coffee.

'Okay. So what have you got in mind for us this time?' he asks, looking suspiciously at me. 'I'm not going to look after any more farm animals Chris so it had better be something small and friendly.'

'It is darling, I promise. It's a dog.'

'What sort of dog? I'm not doing anything big that growls.'

'Well to be honest it's difficult to tell from the photos on the website. He looks a bit of a Heinz 57 to me. Here, have a look,' I say, handing him the ipad.

'You mean he's a mongrel,' replies Rob, glancing at the photo on the screen and taking a swig of coffee from his Dog-Lover's mug.

'I suppose so. Funny though, we don't seem to call them mongrels any more. They're all posh mixed breeds, either cockapoos or labradoodles. This fella looks a bit odd, a bit like a Scottie with long legs. In fact his head looks more Schnautzery, like Molly was.'

'So that makes him either a Scautzer or a Snotty,' replies Rob, smiling at his own joke.

'Very funny. Do you want to know the details or not?'

'Go on then. I don't seem to have any choice. So where does he live?'

'North Yorkshire on the Aire and Calder Canal. That's where my mother grew up and my grandad worked. He was a stevedore in the docks. The house is the lock-keeper's cottage. It'd be lovely Rob, sitting by the water watching the narrowboats sail past the door. I had a wonderful canal holiday years ago on the Kennet and Avon. It was absolutely beautiful chugging along through the countryside watching the wildlife and then mooring up next to a pub for the night.'

The subtle mention of a canal-side pub has the desired effect.

'Sounds fine to me,' replies Rob. 'When do we leave?'

It's six weeks later that we find ourselves following the sat-nav towards Goole. The huge cooling-towers of the nearby power-station at Ferrybridge loom over us, throwing the road ahead into deep shade. Our route is punctuated by derelict buildings and the surrounding landscape appears to have run wild with rose-bay willow-herb and buddleia. This is the industrial north and it seems that we're going to be residing deep in its bowels.

'Well, this is very picturesque darling,' says Rob, glancing at me from the driver's seat with a smirk on his face.

'Oh Rob, I never thought it would be like this. I was expecting it to be pretty,' I reply, my heart sinking as I take in the view ahead of a range of enormous slag-heaps. 'I guess I should have done a bit more research before we accepted, or at least taken more notice of that stuff I read on the Goole web-site.'

'Why? What did it say?'

'Well for a start it said if you've landed on this web-site you were probably looking for Google and it had photos of the local football club with only eight supporters and a burger van. I was so keen to come here because it's where my mother was born.'

'Well, you know what we've learned,' replies Rob reassuringly, 'It's home to someone and it'll be home to us for two weeks so let's make the most of it. We'll be fine.'

As we turn down a narrow lane off the main road we can

see the canal ahead of us, dark and black and wide. Its mirrored surface reflects the dirty, brick face of the huge factory that looms over it, blocking what little sunshine might have been around. This is nothing like the picture-postcard that I'd been imagining.

'That must be the cottage on the right by the lock Rob. Maybe that's them outside?'

'Well that's an idyllic, pastoral scene if ever I saw one,' he replies as we climb out of the car and head towards two figures and a rather grubby-looking white dog that are gathered next to the lock-gates.

Sitting on the lock-beam with her back to us is a woman wearing a sequinned t-shirt and a pair of pink leggings, her hair fetchingly wrapped around plastic rollers, partially covered by a purple headscarf. Next to her on the beam is an extremely scruffy dog who's in the throes of having a hair-cut which doesn't seem to be going too well. He's barking madly and growling at his groomer every time she attempts to get the scissors near him. Large clumps of matted, dirty-white fur keep falling to the ground beneath the lock-beam and he continues to snarl and bark as more of his coat is hacked at with the scissors. A man wearing a sleeveless vest and a pair of jeans is standing next to the canal smoking a cigarette, staring blankly into the black water. The couple seem oblivious to our presence so Rob coughs loudly. The woman turns her head and the dog pricks up his ears, turning immediately in our direction. He's obviously delighted to escape his ordeal and runs up to us barking furiously and snapping at Rob's heels.

'Tyson!' shrieks the woman, but Tyson is far too interested in his visitors to pay her any attention. 'Tyson!' she shrieks again but our new furry friend is by now halfway up Rob's leg investigating his coat pockets.

'I'm so sorry, 'e just wants to say hello. Don't worry, 'e won't hurt you,' says the woman, shuffling towards us. 'You must be

Rob and Christine. Hello, I'm Janice.'

It's only at this point that we realise that there is also a child in the company, a slightly smaller version of his mother, he hides behind her, occasionally peeping out from behind her for a glimpse of us. He has the same disordered appearance as the dog, his hair sticking out in clumps from his chubby, round face, none of it seeming to be of a particularly uniform length. I reckon he must have had the same treatment as the dog.

As we hold out our hands to greet our hostess the man turns in our direction and, after a cursory glance, goes back to staring into the watery depths of the canal.

'That's Stan my husband,' says Janice apologetically. 'Take no notice of 'im. 'E's not a great socialiser. Anyhow, welcome! This is Tyson,' she says ruffling what is left of the fur on the dog's head. 'I was just trying to tidy 'im up before you arrived but I'm afraid 'e doesn't like being groomed, do you lad? And this is our Kevin. Say hello to the lady and gentleman,' she says turning to the boy, but he quickly turns and retreats to the safety of his father's side.

Janice lunges at Tyson, trying to grab him by the scruff, but he bares his teeth at her threateningly, slinks off down the tow-path and disappears into the long grass.

''E does that a lot, just wanders off for ages, so don't worry if you can't find 'im. 'E always comes back in 'is own time. Now come on in and I'll make you a cup o' tea. You must be tired after your journey.'

The front door of the cottage is covered by a small porch and Janice has to turn sideways to get through it. The inner door, which has obviously been attacked by Tyson and been boarded up with a piece of hardboard, opens directly into the tiny sitting-room which is made to look even smaller by the vast collection of ornaments that cover every available surface. The very busy wallpaper depicting large bamboo plants has the effect of making the walls close in on you, leaving you feeling that you'd like to to grab a machete and thrash your way out. The mantlepiece, TV, china-cabinet and built-in shelves are cluttered with more knick-knacks than I've ever seen in one place. Janice must have noticed my jaw drop as she immediately attempts to justify the chaos.

'I know, it's mad isn't it?' she laughs. 'I just love my ornaments. I guess it's become a bit of an obsession. I started collecting horses when I was a little girl and then it were dogs and then pigs and then I guess it sort of grew.'

As we stare incredulously around the room I realise that the collection is actually themed. Not only are there horses and dogs but miniature houses, pigs, fairies, owls, rabbits, all in their hundreds, along with a cabinet full of dolls in national costume. There are even ornaments perched precariously on the ledges above the doors and I'm already feeling nervous about Rob's tendency to clumsiness.

'The family think I'm nuts,' she laughs, 'but I get a lot of pleasure from 'em and that's what counts.'

'Cleaning must be quite a challenge,' I remark, already wondering how the heck anyone can attempt to keep the place free from dust.

'Oh no, I dust 'em all once a week. I know exactly where they go and how many there are. Seven hundred and twenty-three altogether. Drives my Stan mad. I keep going to them car boot sales and coming back with more, I just can't 'elp it. Stan reckons I've got that ODC thing, what do they call it?' she asks, looking searchingly at Rob.

'Obsessive compulsive disorder,' supplies Rob.

'That's right,' she replies. 'Well there's no disorder in 'ere love. They've each got their place and I know exactly where they live. Mind you, it were hell when we had Asbo.'

'Asbo?' queries Rob.

'Yes, he were our cat but little sod used to knock my ornaments onto't floor. Quite deliberate mind! 'E'd sit on't radiator and flip them onto't ground with 'is paw. 'E's dead now poor fella. Fell in't canal and couldn't get out. Stan found him floatin' in't lock. Sad. Now let me show you the kitchen Christine as no doubt it'll be you what's doin't cooking?"

Rob throws me a horrified look as we follow Janice through to the tiny kitchen which can just about accommodate the three of us. It may be small but it's absolutely immaculate and everything is sparkling clean.

'It's all pretty straight forward in 'ere. A bit basic I guess but you should be able to find everything, and 'elp yourself to anything that's in't cupboards and fridge.'

'I'm sure we'll be fine,' I reply. 'Where would we find the nearest shop Janice? Is it far?'

'No love, it's just over't field outside here. You can take a short-cut along 't side of factory but make sure you stick to the path or you'll sink in't slag.'

Rob gives me an alarmed look.

'So what goes on in the factory?' he asks. 'Anything interesting?'

'Shampoo,' replies Janice. 'They used to make pies but some chemical company bought it up six years ago. We've had nothing but trouble ever since. All my roses have changed colour and you should see the state of our cabbages! Stan refuses to eat anything out o't garden now.'

'I'll just go and have a chat with him about the lock system if you'll excuse me?' suggests Rob heading off towards the navigation.

'Stan really needs the rest,' says Janice, propping herself up on the back of one of the chairs. 'We haven't had a break since our Kevin was born but he refuses to leave the lock. It was me daughter's idea to use housesitters and it seemed a really good idea. Tyson'd never cope in't kennels. 'E'd mope and refuse to eat. 'E'll be much happier in 'is own home. The lock'll be fine. It's all centrally controlled now so they'll radio down the navigation if anything's passing through, and a mate of Stan's'll come and handle things so you don't need to worry. There in't much traffic on't water these days since Ferrybridge closed down. We see the occasional commercial barge and some folk in their narrowboats, but who in their right mind'd want to come here for a holiday?'

At that Janice laughs, shrugs her shoulders and climbs the narrow stairs to the bedroom to finish packing while I reflect on her words.

It's a couple of days later, the family having left, that I decide to venture into Goole to do some shopping. Rob has managed to establish an amazing bond with Tyson who has decided that a man with treats is a good thing. Clearly the points system is working in his favour already. This new-found affection all seems very reassuring but he still doesn't seem too keen on me. Any approach is met with a baring of teeth and a warning growl. I leave them sitting happily outside together beside the canal, Rob tackling a code-word and Tyson gnawing on a large stick.

On arriving in the town I manage to find a parking slot without any trouble and head for the nearest supermarket to get a few basic provisions. I return to the car with rather more than we need and a bag of doggy treats for Tyson. Having ventured this far I decide to go for a wander and see if I can find the house where my mother was born. I rescue the address from the bottom of my handbag and set off to explore.

The High Street can only be described as grim. Clearly the town centre is suffering in the same way as many areas of the country. I wander past shops selling cards and mobile phones, interspersed with charity shops. The only building that looks in the slightest bit inviting is a bingo hall. It's depressing and I find myself feeling decidedly saddened by the run-down nature of the place. I poke my nose into a couple of shops and in each case I'm greeted warmly by the shop-assistants. It reminds me of the north south divide and the open, friendly nature of the people in this part of the world.

Turning a corner, I recognise the street name as where my grandparents had once lived and start to wander down the road in search of their house. The majority of the small terraced houses, once uniform red brick, have been modernised with PVC windows and leaded lights. In places the red brick has been faced with dressed stone but the street has been well cared for and clearly there is pride in the appearance of the houses. I manage to find number 38 which, to my pleasure, still has the original plaster-work and the date of the cottages on the wall. I never knew my grand-parents so there's a tinge of sadness finding myself outside their front door.

I turn to head back to the town, realising that Rob must be wondering where I've got to. It's then that I notice a shop window surprisingly displaying all manner of exotic underwear. Quite how such an emporium has found its way into the side streets of Goole is a mystery but, reflecting on the rather dull appearance of my M&S matching sets, I decide to take a peek inside.

To my amazement the shop is an Aladdin's cave of lingerie. I walk around the various stands wondering who on earth buys this stuff. I can't imagine what sort of women cavort around the bedroom in some of these outfits, and there seems to be a wide range of bras in such large cup sizes that I'm beginning to feel somewhat inadequate. It's then that I'm suddenly approached by a very stern looking woman, probably in her late sixties, dressed in a blazer, pleated skirt and sensible brogues with a tape measure round her neck. Her grey hair is cut severely in a short bob that reminds me of my old Latin mistress.

'Can I help you?' she enquires in a rather brusque tone.

'Er, no thank you, I was just browsing,' I reply nervously, attempting a smile.

'What size are you?' asks the woman, her broad accent rather evident in spite of her obvious effort to disguise it.

I find this a rather intimate and somewhat embarrassing question to have to answer, especially in public as there are a couple of other women in the shop and, more alarmingly, a man.

'38A,' I whisper in reply.

'38A?' she queries in a voice loud enough to be heard by the other customers. 'You never are. Come 'ere love.' And with that she opens the front of my jacket, clasps her hands firmly around my ribs just below my bust and pronounces with great confidence, 'You never are! You're a 36B. You've been wearin't wrong size. Get in't cubicle!'

I'm so startled by her command that I feel unable to refuse. She pulls the curtain determinedly across the doorway with a flourish and, within seconds, is thrusting all manner of bras through the gap. I gape in wonder at the vast array of garments that are being delivered, but now feel captive. By the selection that she's feeding through the curtain she clearly imagines that I have an extremely raunchy sex-life. It seems that the only way to escape is to buy something and get out before she starts on the dominatrix outfits or the latex.

'Er, I'll take this one,' I say, handing the least provocative bra that I can find back through the curtain. I dress quickly and head for the till.

'That'll be £47.99 including the matching briefs,' she says, handing me the card machine.

I've never spent so much on underwear in my life and goodness knows how I'm going to explain this to Rob. It's bad enough having to justify my occasional £11.99 at M&S. Maybe I'll just bury the bag in the boot of the car and deal with it when we get home.

It's a good couple of hours before I arrive back at base to find Rob still sitting outside by the lock, Tyson sleeping quietly by his side.

'Alright darling? How was Google?' Rob asks.

'Sad,' I reply. 'I wanted it to feel homely for my mum's sake but it's just so run down. The people were lovely but the town's clearly suffering like so many places that we've visited. Anyhow, what about you? What have you been up to?'

'Not a lot really. I tried to take Tyson for his walk but it became a bit tricky so we turned back.'

'Tricky? How can a walk down a towpath be tricky?'

'Because it was cluttered with fishermen all along the bank. It seems that there's a competition on this weekend. There's a dirty great double-decker bus parked next to the factory and there must be at least fifty guys sitting on little stools at regular intervals all along the bank clutching huge, fibreglass rods. It was such an obstacle course and they were all so blooming grumpy if I needed them to shift their rods to let us past that we gave up and came home. They're a morose bunch.'

'I wonder what they find to catch in these murky waters?' I ask.

'I did ask one bloke. Apparently it's stuff like roach and perch but I bet they get a good few pike too.'

'So when you say competition, what exactly happens? Is it the person who catches the biggest fish?'

'I think it's the weight of the entire catch but there are probably prizes for individual fish as well poor things. I couldn't do it, Chris, it's cruel. Imagine having a dirty great hook through your lip. Anyhow, you know I don't like eating fish so there wouldn't be much point me taking up angling. The kit must cost them a fortune and as for the bait, yuk! I saw one guy grabbing a handful of live maggots and throwing them into the water and then using the same hand to eat his crisps!'

'Oh, that's disgusting. Imagine if you lost concentration!' I shudder.

'And would you believe it, some of them have got video cameras set up on tripods overlooking their pitch?'

'Whatever for?'

'I guess they're hoping to capture the action when they hook the prize catch. It's another world really. Oh, and by the way, I'm afraid I had a little accident while you were out,' announces Rob hesitantly.

'Accident? Have you hurt yourself?'

'No, I'm fine, but I'm afraid I've managed to break one of Janice's ornaments.'

'Oh Rob. How on earth did that happen?' ( I can feel the exasperation rise as I speak.)

'I'd left the front door open and the wind must have caught the inner door so it slammed shut. One of the things that was perched above the door fell down and smashed. It was an accident.'

'Dare I ask what it was?'

'One of those little green dogs, the one that looked a bit like Tyson. I could try to fix it with superglue but I think it's too badly chipped. I left the pieces on the kitchen table. See what you think.'

The green dog is sadly, and worryingly, beyond repair.

'Do you think she'd notice or shall we just keep quiet about it?' asks Rob.

'Yes I do think she'd notice and how come this has become 'we'? You're the one who broke it.'

'It wasn't deliberate Chris. It could have happened to anyone.'

'I appreciate that Rob, but the fact is that it happened to you.'

I pick up the remaining pieces of the ornament and, on trying to reassemble it, notice some lettering on the base. I can just manage to pick out the word Sylvac. I reach for my phone and eBay.

'You're in luck,' I say placing the image of a green dog in front of Rob. '£15.99 plus £6 postage. We can hopefully get it delivered before they get back. Just think yourself lucky it wasn't a rare edition.'

'Oh you star Chris! But £22 for that? It's a hideous looking thing.'

'Not to Janice it isn't. I'll find the address and get it ordered straight away. You can give me your pocket-money later,' I smile.

Our strange life on the canal proves to be an education. We lie awake at night as the cottage shudders every time the hammers at the local glass factory hit their target. It becomes strangely soothing as they work to a rhythm that eventually leads us into sleep. The boats that pass the door are mainly commercial barges, but we also see the occasional narrow-boat, privately owned craft, this area being of no interest to the hire companies in the Midlands that let out their boats for big money. There's something about the industrial beauty that I love, maybe because of my roots. In spite of the inevitable scars on the landscape I find it mysteriously alluring.

One afternoon a beautifully maintained narrowboat sails past, bedecked with brightly-painted cans, all in the traditional primary colours of the waterways, its roof decorated with colourful window-boxes. An elderly couple wave to us from the bows.

'Lovely day!' they shout.

'Isn't it!' I reply.

'So where are you heading?' asks Rob, always curious to know where folk hail from.

'We're off to Kidderminster to buy a carpet,' replies the woman at the rudder.

'Kidderminster! That's a bit of a trek isn't it?' Rob shouts.

'Only 200 miles. We reckon we can do it in 13 days,' replies the man. 'You can afford to take life slowly at our time in life,' he laughs. 'Cheerio! Enjoy the rest of your day.'

'Have you noticed how boat-people are so much happier than fishermen?' observes Rob. 'I've been conducting a survey. People on boats always wave and exchange a greeting.

Fishermen just grunt and refuse to communicate.'

'Well maybe people who fish choose to do so because they like being alone and don't want to have to talk to people,' I suggest. 'It must be lovely to live on a boat,' I muse, 'pootling along at three miles an hour, stopping off at a canal-side pub for lunch, changing the view from your window every day. I reckon I could get used to that. Maybe we should buy a narrow-boat?'

'Pubs maybe, but I couldn't cope living in such a confined space Chris. I'd get claustrophobia and I'd be terrified of falling in one of those locks and meeting a watery end like poor Asbo. No, I'll settle for house-sitting, it's a lot safer and more comfortable and I get to have a furry friend or two,' he says, leaning down to stroke Tyson's head. 'Poor lad, he looks as though he's been attacked with that weird hair-cut. Come on boy, let's go for our walk. Hopefully there won't be any grumpy fishermen about. I'm going to pop him on the lead today Chris cos he was showing rather a lot of interest in those mallards that are nesting down past the factory and I don't want him jumping in after them.'

'Okay. I'll start on dinner while you're out so don't wander too far the pair of you,' I warn him as they set off down the tow-path.

I watch from the kitchen window as Rob ambles off, Tyson trotting along dutifully at his heels, seemingly happy to be on the end of a lead. It's when I see Rob with an animal that I start to wonder if we should get another dog. He's never happier than when he's got a furry companion but we're both too nervous of the inevitable heartache involved in losing another animal.

It's while I'm lost in thought that I look back down the towpath and see a dark figure approaching, carrying something seemingly heavy in his arms. As he draws closer I realise to my horror that it's Rob and he's carrying Tyson. I rush out to meet them only to discover that both of them are absolutely sodden, clearly having somehow fallen in the water.

'Oh my God! Are you alright? Whatever's happened?'

Rob's finding it difficult to speak and keeps spitting into the grass. I reach out to take Tyson from him but Tyson bares his teeth at me and growls.

'He's okay,' splutters Rob. 'We took a tumble into the water that's all.'

'That's all? But you're absolutely soaked and goodness knows what you've got on your clothes. It looks like oil.'

'Diesel,' coughs Rob. 'It's diesel that's been leaking from that barge that's moored outside the factory. We fell in just beside it and I got a mouthful. My throat feels really raw. Poor Tyson's got it all over his coat too if you look. It's going to be a job to get him cleaned up. Just as well he's usually a bit grubby.'

'Well let's get the pair of you sorted. I think a shower's the best solution. Get your kit off and you can go in together and then you can tell me what happened.'

As man and dog undergo a vigorous shampooing, Tyson being surprisingly co-operative, Rob explains that Tyson had caught sight of the ducks again and lunged unexpectedly, pulling him off balance.

'There was nothing I could do. He just leapt into the water pulling me after him. Thank God it wasn't too deep or we'd never have got out. I just hope we can get the oil off him. As for having had a mouthful of the Aire and Calder, I'll probably contract something awful like Weill's disease. You do realise that rat's pee carries bacteria that can kill?'

'Yes Rob but that's in stagnant water and I'm sure you'll be fine once we've got you cleaned up.'

'I'm already shivering,' he shouts from behind the shower door. 'Maybe I've got a fever?'

'Rob, you're fine. You just got cold because you fell in the canal. For heaven's sake stop worrying!'

A couple of hours later the pair of them are squeaky clean and are dozing contentedly in front of the coal-fire that I've lit for them. The smell of the fire reminds me of my childhood and of toasting crumpets on a long wire fork. All is well with the world.

As we reach the final day of our sit Rob seems to have recovered from his ordeal. Tyson looks as though he's been to the poodle-parlour as his coat is now clean and silky following his shower. There's only one outstanding worry. We're still awaiting the delivery of the eBay purchase.

'The post's usually here by now Chris, we're cutting it a bit fine. What if it doesn't arrive today? We'll have to come clean with Janice about the breakage if it doesn't.'

'They're not due back until late afternoon, I'm sure it'll have arrived by then,' I reply reassuringly, but quietly worrying that Rob might be right.

'I'll just pop out the back and put the rest of our stuff in the car then, love,' says Rob.

Just as he disappears there's a knock on the front door. Tyson shoots out of the sitting room and begins to growl and bark furiously.

'Hang on a minute, I'm coming!' I shout through the door as I nervously grab hold of Tyson's collar and quickly lock him in the kitchen. 'Sorry about that,' I apologise, opening the front door.

To my relief there stands the postman holding a small parcel in his hand. I could cheerfully hug him.

'Oh am I glad to see you!' I exclaim.

'Delivery for Mrs Baird?' he queries looking me up and down.

'Yes thanks. That's me. We've been looking after the house while the owners are away,' I reply, my face having broken into a large smile at the relief of seeing the parcel.

'Enjoying yourselves I hope?' he asks, moving towards me and leaning up against the doorway while talking to the top button of my blouse. He's clearly getting on a bit but the look in his eyes tells me he still thinks he's a bit of a lad, even in his sixties.

'Er, yes, thank you,' I reply, feeling decidedly uncomfortable by his proximity and taking hold of my necklace in the hope of obscuring any of my chest that might be on show.

'So, you staying long?' he asks, placing his foot firmly on the threshold and licking his lower lip with his tongue.

'Actually we're leaving today,' I reply curtly, attempting to sound business-like.

Bang on cue I can hear Rob returning from the car and my mounting discomfort turns to relief. My man has come to rescue me from the lecherous advances of the Royal Mail.

'Darling?' he calls from the back door in an unusually seductive voice. 'I was just wondering when I'm going to have the pleasure of seeing you in these?' as he sidles up behind me holding aloft my new black lace ensemble.

# 14

# WHEN LIFE GIVES YOU LEMONS

The photos on the website are of a picture-postcard Tuscany. Rolling hills dotted with terracotta farmhouses and rows of tall cypresses leading down dusty avenues to cool, white villas. Several cats and two dogs can be seen basking in the shade of some pine trees and in the background are two terracotta pots of lemons. A table laid with a bottle of wine, two glasses and a plate of cheese and cold meats has already got my imagination in overdrive. I cannily leave the laptop open on the kitchen table so that Rob can't avoid seeing the images when he comes downstairs and wait quietly in the adjoining room.

'Wow! That looks fabulous!' comes the cry. 'I think you've struck gold there Chris. You've got to apply for that one.'

'It's all very well saying that Rob but they've already had over thirty applicants. I don't know how I missed it when it was first advertised. Still, no harm in trying I guess, but don't build your hopes up.'

Two days later when I open the computer there's an email for me that reads, 'You have a new message.' I can't contain my excitement but when I read the reply my heart sinks.

'Thank you so much for your interest, but I'm afraid we have now found a house-sitter. Best wishes Rebecca and Patrizio.'

I try not to get too upset but I'm actually gutted. My imagination had already transported us to Italy with the pair of us sitting in the shade of the pines drinking Chianti and tucking in to that plate of cheese. I share the bad news and am surprised to see just how upset Rob is too.

'So where did we go wrong Chris?' he asks. 'We've got

brilliant references, you speak good enough Italian, we know the country. I don't understand why we didn't get it.'

'Darling you have to remember that we're not the only folk who applied and there are literally hundreds of other sitters who are just as well-qualified as we are. There'll be other opportunities, so try not to get too upset.'

Over the next few days I try to put into practice the advice that I've offered Rob, but deep down there's a gnawing sadness. I busy myself with cleaning the house and tidying the garden and in between jobs keep returning to the web-site in search of something equally enticing. Some seven weeks later we're feeling resigned to spending the summer at home. Although the web-site's flooded with opportunities, Tuscany has spoilt it for us and nowhere else seems to be anywhere near as appealing.

It's while checking the web-site one morning after breakfast that I notice an envelope against my inbox. I don't recall applying for anything recently but have been known to press the 'apply' button for all manner of weird and wonderful locations in the late evening, following a couple of glasses of wine. Embarrassingly I hadn't picked up on the fact that the delightful cockapoo puppy that I'd fallen for a couple of months ago lived in South Korea. However, this message is a mystery. I click on the 'open' button and read:

*'Hi Christine and Robert,*
*I hope this finds you both well. We were wondering if, by any wonderful chance, you could still be available to house-sit for us? The couple who had agreed to come have unfortunately had to pull out due to a bereavement. I realise that this is very last minute but we'd be delighted if you could help us out. An early response would be much appreciated.*
*Best wishes*
*Rebecca'*

Just three days later we disembark the plane at Pisa, both still excited by our good fortune. As we descend the stairs of the plane we're hit by the blast of heat that bounces up from the tarmac. It feels so welcome after the dreary grey that we've left behind at home. Walking out of the arrivals hall we can see a woman waving at us. It's clearly Rebecca, who's kindly come to meet us: an ex-pat, according to the web-site, who's lived in Italy for many years having married an Italian journalist.

'Ciao Christine!' she says, greeting me warmly with a hug and a kiss on each cheek. 'Thank you so much for coming! We never thought we'd manage to find someone at such short notice. We can't thank you enough for helping us out!'

'Our pleasure!' says Rob, clearly enjoying the warm welcome and smiling broadly at Rebecca. She's a stunning red-head, probably in her late forties, and the warmth of her tanned skin adds to her natural beauty.

'It's just under a two hour drive,' explains our hostess, 'and I'm afraid the air-con's packed in on the car. I've got plenty of water on board so hopefully we'll survive.'

As we drive through the golden folds of the Tuscan hills Rebecca is able to outline what will need doing while she and her husband are away. Apparently Patrizio has already left and she is to join him the next day in Athens where their daughter is working in a refugee camp. There are nine cats and two dogs, Yasma and Arpa. She reassures us that the cats are pretty feral but like to call in to be fed and that the dogs will need walking in the early morning or late evening when it's cool. What really matters to her is the garden.

'I'm growing vegetables and they need plenty of water when it's so hot that I'm afraid you'll need to give everything a good soak twice a day if that's okay? It doesn't help them being planted under the trees as they steal so much of the water. We're actually on well water but the levels are quite healthy at the moment so there shouldn't be a problem. Anyhow, I can show you everything when we get home.'

Just over two hours later the three of us extract ourselves from the Fiat 500, our clothes soaked with sweat. My hair has plastered itself to my forehead and I smell pretty revolting. Rob has turned an uncomfortable shade of red and has rivulets of sweat running down his neck. Somehow Rebecca carries the hot and sweaty look in a much more attractive and decidedly raunchy way. Needless to say the beads of sweat rolling down her ample cleavage have not gone unnoticed by Rob.

As soon as we shut the car doors the two dogs appear, barking excitedly and keen to check us out. Rebecca calms them down and introduces our new charges.

'This is Arpa,' she says, making a fuss of a gangly-legged, creamy-coloured hound, 'and this is Yasma.'

Yasma, a boxer with a protruding lower jaw, gives us what can only be described as a smile. Her rather unfortunate appearance is strangely appealing and she cocks her head on one side while we let her sniff at us. Soon she's found the treats in Rob's trouser-pocket and is licking his hand.

'You've got a friend already!' laughs Rebecca. 'She's an embarrassment. Come on in and let me show you your room and then I'm sure you'd welcome a shower.'

Just as we're about to enter, she pauses to point out two large, terracotta pots, one either side of the back door, each containing a small lemon tree.

'These are my babies,' she says proudly. 'It's the first time I've managed to get fruit on them, but look, I've got three lemons coming on this plant and two on this one! I'm so excited!'

I'm rather envious of her being able to grow lemons, they seem so exotic. The fruits are already quite sizeable and I can understand the anticipation and excitement of being able to pick them later in the year.

'Don't worry, we'll keep a close eye on them,' I reassure her.

The house is a typical Tuscan farmhouse on three storeys with an extensive, cool cantina below the ground floor. Numerous cats have tucked themselves away in shady spots around the house where the tiled floors ensure that it's delightfully cool. We climb the stairs to the guest room at the top of the house where Rob opens a pair of green, wooden shutters. There's a stunning view over the surrounding vineyards and the towers of San Gimignano can just be made out in the far distance. A tractor is trundling along between the rows of vines creating a cloud of dust in its wake. It's like something out of a film and I can't believe that this is to be our home for the next three weeks. Rob comes up behind me and snuggles into my neck.

'Well done, that woman,' he says. 'It was clearly meant to be after all.'


Two days later, alone in our new home, we've already fallen into the daily routine of walking the dogs, feeding the cats and watering the garden. The intense heat dictates what we do, as it becomes so fierce by early afternoon that we're driven indoors, where we're lulled into having a siesta. The dogs sleep for most of the day, Yasma amusingly stretched out on the plastic picnic table in the garden that sits under the pine trees. Arpa prefers the earth floor of the cantina where she's often joined by a couple of the cats.

It's about three o'clock one afternoon, my having ventured out to sweep the patio of its carpet of pine needles, that I hear a strange pinging noise, akin to someone plucking the strings of a musical instrument. I can't work out where it's coming from when suddenly something lands on my head. Afraid that it might be an insect I run to find Rob and ask him to have a look in case I get stung.

'Nope, it looks like a seed,' he says, holding a small, brown seed-case in his hand. I pick at the outer coating to see what's inside and am surprised to find a hard, sooty, inner case. Breaking into it I'm amazed to discover a shiny, ivory-coloured pine-nut.

'Of course!' I exclaim. 'It's the pine-cones flinging their seeds out that I can hear. Wow! Let's see if we can find some more. These things cost a fortune in the shops and we've got our own supply!'

The pair of us wander around under the pines searching for the seed-cases. Soon we're joined by Arpa who has picked up on our activity. Within seconds she's got her nose to the ground and is sniffing around in the carpet of pine-needles. She deftly picks up a seed and is soon crushing the nut in her jaw. She's clearly very experienced in seeking them out as she's already managed to crunch her way through several, while I'm still trying to get the outer shell off mine.

After a couple of days the hunt for the pine-nuts has become a game. On cue, at three in the afternoon, the cones start to ping their seeds onto the garden and my pinoli hound and I have a race to see who can find the most. She loves the fun and I can only marvel at the power of her nose.

Each evening, as the temperature starts to drop, we take the dogs for a walk through the vineyards and into the woods. We've been warned to keep an eye open for adders and to ensure that we always wear wellingtons when we go out. This is not the most comfortable garb when it's still 36 degrees and you're desperate to expose your feet to the air. However, the idea of being bitten by a snake is enough of a deterrent, so we follow the advice that we've been given.

Emerging from the woodland we're somewhat bemused to find a full-sized football-pitch in front of us, complete with changing-room and an elaborate sprinkler system. It's been beautifully maintained but seems bizarrely out of place here and we can't imagine why it's been constructed in such a remote location. Partly hidden from view is a small building resembling a garage and outside are two, apparently very elderly, people sitting on plastic chairs underneath a faded sun umbrella. We smile and greet them with a wave but they eye us suspiciously. They don't respond and we're left feeling that we're intruding on their territory. On closer inspection I notice that the woman, her skin brown and leathery from the sun, is wearing a long skirt that is hanging below her ankles in the dust. On her top half she is strangely wearing a bra on top of her vest. The man, dressed in an old football shirt and drawing heavily on a cigarette, stares coldly at us. Their apparent hostility is unnerving, so we continue our walk making a deviation on our return to avoid them.

The night is delightfully balmy and we can't resist sitting out under the stars drinking yet another glass of wine. It's well after eleven when we eventually go to bed having chained the dogs up in the yard. Not long after we've fallen asleep I'm woken by Rob who's thrashing around in the bed, waving his arms about furiously. I assume that he's having one of his car-chase dreams.

'Whatever's the matter?' I ask wearily, propping myself up on my pillow.

'Bloody mosquitoes!' replies Rob exasperatedly. 'I'm sure I've just been bitten.'

'Well they only make that buzzing noise after they've fed on you.'

'They're buzzing alright, I'm going to be eaten alive Chris. You know how mozzies like me.'

'Well I did warn you to close the shutters before we came to bed. It was your idea to leave them open,' I reply, my tone clearly devoid of sympathy.

I have to acknowledge that Rob does seem to be a target when the mosquitoes are at large. For some unknown reason my poor man is a magnet to the dreaded zanzare.

'I hate to say it Rob but I remember reading that they've been having a big problem with zanzare tigre in Tuscany.'

'And what, dare I ask, are zanzare tigre?'

'They feed during the day as well as at night-time I'm afraid.'

'Oh brilliant! So I'm going to have my blood sucked while

I'm trying to have a siesta as well as at night now. You know how badly I react to mozzie bites Chris. I'm going to be an absolute mess.'

Unfortunately Rob is right. After only three days his skin has erupted into huge weals and dark scabs have developed where he's been scratching. In spite of coating himself liberally in insect repellant the stripey predators zoom in on their target leaving Rob looking like a human pin-cushion.

'Listen to this Chris,' he calls from the cool of the kitchen where he's busy Googling the best way to deter the beasts. 'The tiger mosquito is known to transmit pathogens and viruses, such as the yellow fever virus, dengue fever, Chikungunya fever and Usutu virus.' You do realise that I'm probably going to get some terminal disease.'

'You're not Rob. I know it's no fun but you're not going to die from yellow fever or anything else for that matter. Here, put some of this on,' and I hand him a bottle of Avon's Skin So Soft.

'Skin So Soft! What good's that going to do me? I need to stop the little beasts biting me, not undergo some fancy, moisturising, beauty treatment.'

'According to the internet this is the best repellent available, apparently even the SAS use it,' I inform him. 'I bought three bottles before we left as a precaution and I don't want to see it going to waste, so you'd better give it a go. Here.' And at that I spray a coating of oil on his arm.

Reluctantly Rob spreads a liberal amount on his face, arms and legs.

'Good grief, I smell dreadful.'

'Well hopefully the mozzies'll think so too and give you a wide berth,' I reply. 'It's either that or that highly toxic Jungle Formula and I really don't want us doused in chemicals.'

'So how come they don't eat you?'

'Marmite.

'What do you mean, Marmite? Don't tell me you've been

smothering yourself with the stuff!'

'No, but I eat plenty of it and it raises my vitamin B levels so the mozzies stay away. You ought to develop a taste for it.'

'No Chris, I refuse. It's disgusting stuff. I'll stick with the Skin So Soft.'

Our new home is one of only four houses clustered closely together on the hillside. One of them, apparently owned by the local church, is sadly derelict, the other two occupied by local families who, we have been informed, choose not to speak to one another. Having met each of them I can understand why. They fit the English expression of 'chalk and cheese' perfectly. Across the dust track from our house live Giovanni and his wife Rosa. A local boy made good, Giovanni now owns an immaculate, stone-built house that has been renovated to perfection. It's surrounded by huge lawns and is approached via a long drive, lined with terracotta pots full of plants bearing geraniums and citrus fruits. There must be nearing two hundred of them. Every evening the sprinkler system is switched on at dusk and carries on well into the early hours of the morning. The lawns are lush and green, the plants healthy and already bearing fruit that seems to swell on a daily basis. In the centre of the property is an enticing swimming-pool complete with plastic shark. Medallion Man, as we have christened Giovanni, spends all his spare hours tending the garden and the pool wearing nothing but a gold necklace and a pair of Speedos, whilst Rosa seems to do nothing but sweep the numerous patios and paths. I feel positively guilty lying in the sun with a good book while they labour in the heat.

On the other side of our wall is a traditional Tuscan country house, situated somewhat below ours so that the view from our garden is unspoilt. It's the home of Grazia and Vale, a midwife and doctor, probably in their early thirties, and the doctor's elderly parents, Gina and her husband Michele. Theirs is a simple life but they're most welcoming and generous in wanting us to join them regularly for meals. We eat, rather unusually, in the garage as it offers a cool space to escape the fierce Tuscan sun. Both Grazia and Vale spend half of each year in Bolivia on an Italian medical project but during the summer their parents and Vale's brother move out of Florence in order to escape the oppressive heat and settle into the country retreat.

Nonna Gina takes a shine to me and, every afternoon after her siesta, I hear her cry over the wall,

'Christina, vieni qui!'

This is my instruction to attend my afternoon cookery lesson. I adore this lady and can think of no happier time than sitting outside watching her prepare the pasta for the evening meal. I perch on the wall that encloses an enormous water tank where the ducks swim and the turkeys appear occasionally to drink. I sit in the shade and watch her experienced hands at work producing all manner of wonderful meals, occasionally being summoned to lend a hand with the preparation. I'm in heaven.

Every morning before the sun gets hot, and every evening once it has started to cool down, we water the garden, liberally soaking the ground around the peppers, tomatoes and aubergines and paying particular attention to the two lemon trees outside the back door.

'The fruits are definitely beginning to swell,' remarks Rob. 'Rebecca'll be really pleased when she gets back.'

At bedtime, or when we need to leave the house, Yasma and Arpa are chained up in the yard. They have plenty of space to roam around but spend most of the day sleeping. Arpa and I continue our now customary hunt for the pinoli and I'm getting close to having enough to make my very own pesto.

One afternoon, while we're lying in the garden sunbathing, a sudden, terrified scream erupts from the garden next door. I recognise the voice as Nonna Gina who is clearly absolutely hysterical.

'Oh mio dio! Il serpente! Maledetto serpentaccio!' we hear her cry. Arpa and Yasma rush to the garden wall and start to bark furiously having been woken from their sleep.

'My goodness, she doesn't sound too happy!' says Rob, raising his head from the ground where he's lying. 'I wonder what all that's about?'

'Well if my understanding's correct she's seen the snake again,' I reply.

'Snake, what snake? And what do you mean, again?'

'Apparently there's a dirty great water snake lives in the water tank and he occasionally likes to slither around the garden. Grazia told me.'

'Well thanks for letting me know Chris! And how big is this snake?'

'According to Grazia it's quite a big brute, about as thick as a man's arm, but it's quite harmless. The problem is that they can't persuade Nonna Gina that it's not dangerous.'

'Good grief, it sounds terrifying. Why didn't you tell me? I mean if it had come slithering over the grass while I was sunbathing I could have died of fright!'

'Oh don't exaggerate Rob. Anyhow, it hasn't come slithering across the grass and you're perfectly safe even if it does.'

Later that evening I add the word 'terrorizzatto' to my list of new vocabulary, or, in dear Nonna Gina's case, 'terrorizzatta'.

After a couple of weeks it feels as though we've always lived in the house. The cats come and go as the mood takes them and gradually build up the confidence to approach us and, in a couple of cases, even honour us with their company, curling up beside us in the garden. Capuccino, a beautiful Siamese, likes to talk to Rob, becoming more and more vocal as it approaches feeding time. Saddam and Raisa are inseparable and can always be found curled up together, nose to tail. There are regular spats between the less domesticated members of the menagerie and at times the hush of the afternoon is punctuated by bouts of hissing and yelling as territories are invaded or a squabble erupts. When we fill their feeding bowls all nine of them appear as if from nowhere then, having eaten, disappear into the cool of the shadows.

Yasma and Arpa are clearly happy with the new arrangements and, whilst out walking, trot happily along off their leads, coming dutifully when called. Fortunately they're bi-lingual but I enjoy practising my Italian on them. Arpa has definitely become my dog, walking by my side and regularly checking on me with an upward glance that I interpret as love. Rob's not so sure.

'It's only because you've got treats in your pocket,' he says, but I'm convinced that we have a special bond that somehow springs from nowhere with an animal.

In the early morning, while we're out walking in the olive-groves, a wonderful, romantic mist shrouds the silvery trees in cobwebs. The chain-link fencing that surrounds the football pitch is covered with a myriad of snails that have glued themselves securely to the metal posts in order to conserve moisture.

'By the way, I forgot to tell you,' I say. 'I've found out the story behind all this.'

'Oh, and?'

'Well, you remember the old couple that we saw sitting outside the garage the other day? Apparently they had the pitch constructed in memory of their son who got killed in a motorcycle accident. They created it for the local football team that he played for who'd never had their own ground.'

'Gosh, that's a tragic story Chris. How sad, but what a generous tribute.'

A sudden loud bang interrupts our conversation. It's a gun-shot and, before we know it, Arpa is off, tearing across the vineyard towards the woods. She's clearly connected with her innate desire to hunt and we realise that there's little chance of us finding her in the depths of several hundred hectares of woodland. We quickly grab hold of Yasma before she heads off to join her.

'Now what do we do?' asks Rob, his voice already indicating his concern. 'We'll never find her in there and, if she's got scent of something, goodness knows how long she'll be gone.'

Rob cups his hands to his mouth and calls out, 'Aaaaaaarpa.' His cry becomes immediately muffled by the dense undergrowth.

'I hate to say it but you're wasting your energy Rob. Worrying though it might be I don't think there's anything we can do immediately. It's pointless trying to follow and call for her if she's on the scent of something. A dog doesn't hear when its basic instinct kicks in. Besides which, there are clearly people hunting in there. I think it's probably better if we just head home and hope that she turns up. If she doesn't we'll have to somehow put out an alert, but we'll worry about that later.'

The day is long and hot and neither of us are able to rest. It's one of the worst case scenarios: we've lost someone's animal that was in our care. I call next door and explain what's happened and all of the family are very reassuring. She's done it before and she always comes back. Try not to worry and just sit tight for the time being.

As dusk falls and the zanzare start buzzing we're beginning to get seriously worried.

'What if she's been shot Chris?' asks Rob, clearly concerned by now.

'Rob, my imagination's already running riot, I really don't need you to up my angst,' I snap back at him.

'I'm sorry love, I'm just worried sick about her and even more worried about how we explain things to Rebecca. Do you think we should ring her and tell her what's happened?'

'I don't see the point at this stage. She can't do anything from Athens and it'll only make her worry. Let's leave it until morning.

I think I'm going to turn in soon anyhow. I'm shattered.'

'Okay. I'll see you upstairs in a minute.'

As I climb the stairs, my thoughts tying knots in my head, I suddenly pick up on a strange noise coming from our bedroom. It's a loud wheezing, as though someone's having difficulty breathing. As I approach the room I'm actually feeling quite spooked. I push open the door, trying not to make too much noise, unsure of what I'm going to find. The light from the landing shines onto the bed and there, curled in a comfy ball, is Arpa. She looks up sleepily as if to object to being wakened. Suddenly realising that she's out of bounds, and likely to be in trouble for straying to the top of the house, she plays for the sympathy card and rolls over onto her back.

'Arpa, you monster!' I cry, the tears welling up. 'Rob!' I shout. 'Rob, come here!'

'Are you alright darling? Whats' the matter?'

'Come and see,' I cry, the tears rolling. 'She's here. Arpa's here.'

Rob rushes up the stairs and looks in disbelief at my pinoli hound. She's lying on her back, all four paws in the air, tail beating madly against the bed, her tongue lolling.

'You absolute horror Arpa,' I sniffle, wiping my eyes on her head. 'You have no idea how worried we've been.'

She kisses my face and I kiss hers in return. Soon we're all three fast asleep, Arpa carefully sandwiched between us.

The following day there's a knock at the door. It's Nonna Gina who's come to see if Arpa has returned. She's overjoyed and says we must go round to eat with them that evening to celebrate. Having bought some lemons in the local town I decide to make some lemon curd to take as a small gift for Nonna as it's something, I have discovered, that is unknown to her. I find a reliable recipe online and am soon stirring the contents of a glass bowl filled with lemons, butter, eggs and sugar, perched over a pan of simmering water.

'You wouldn't believe how different the lemons are here Rob,' I tell him as I continue to stir the bright yellow sauce gently. 'The zest is so firm you get so much more flavour and there was lots more juice than we ever find because they're so fresh. It's going to taste wonderful.'

Two hours later I'm still stirring gently and am now worrying that the sauce is never going to thicken.

'It must be because there's so much juice,' I wail. 'We might just have to pour it over some ice-cream.'

'I reckon I could cope with that, I shouldn't worry too much if I was you sweetheart. It'll taste good whatever happens.'

Later that evening we pull the back door behind us, chain up the dogs, having left them each with a chew, and head for Grazia's, me clutching my jar of sort-of lemon curd for Nonna Gina. She's so thrilled that she can't resist taking the top off and spooning some into her mouth. She gives me a big smile, presses her finger into her cheek and appears to drill it into her face.

'What's all that about?' asks Rob.

'It's a compliment. Italian sign-language. It means she thinks it's really good,' I reply.

'I told you it would work out,' says Rob smugly.

We sit down to dinner in the garage, a veritable feast washed down with the family's own wine. Michele disappears inside and returns with his guitar and we sit back and listen to him singing old Italian folk songs.

'Paradiso,' I whisper to Rob, laying my head on his shoulder.

But suddenly our paradiso is shattered as there, at my side, gazing fondly up at me is Arpa. Rob and I look at each other in bewilderment.

'How on earth?' he asks, staring at me.

Nonna Gina explains that Arpa has obviously heard my voice down below the house and decided to join us. But not only has she managed to clear the fence and leap down from the high wall, she's obviously broken her chain as well, as a length of it is still dangling from her collar. The family laugh and we all make a fuss of Arpa who obviously thinks she's come out tops again. She lies down contentedly under the table on my feet and stays there for the rest of the evening.

It's a good while after midnight when we manage to grope our way back to the house in semi-darkness having forgotten our torch. As we approach the yard the security lights flicker on, but, as we head for the back door, Rob trips over something in his path. To our horror, there on the patio are the two terracotta pots, lying on their sides, fortunately unbroken but, lying haphazardly among the pine needles are Rebecca's prize lemons. I feel like crying but maybe it's the wine that makes me see the vaguely funny side of things.

'Well, you know what they say Chris. When life gives you lemons make lemon curd,' chuckles Rob.

'Actually there's a much better saying,' I reply, glaring at him. 'When life gives you lemons, put them in the freezer and then throw them at the person who's irritating you. Now get up those stairs before I squirt them in your eyes!'

And at that Rob scales the stairs three at a time laughing.

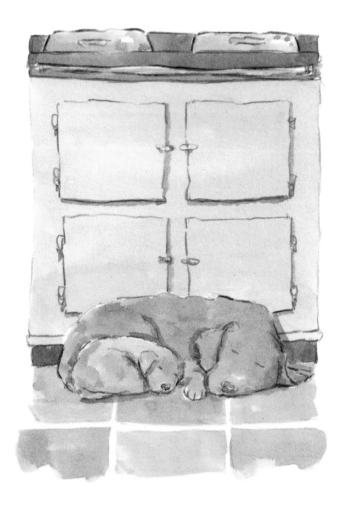

# 15

## PUPPY LOVE

'Okay, so what's on the agenda this morning?' asks Rob, settling down by the fire with his hands wrapped round his Dog-Lover's mug. 'Go on, put me out of my misery Chris.'

'Well, I've short-listed three sits but I'm a bit wary of travel at this time of year. You know what it's like coming up to Christmas. The airports are hell on earth and then there's the problem with the weather. I don't think we should be looking at being too ambitious but it would be nice to be somewhere other than home for Christmas.'

'Go on then, start at the top and work down.'

'Well, there's a bungalow in Chipping Camden with an elderly cat and some fish. According to the blurb the cat needs twice-daily insulin injections for diabetes.'

'No way am I injecting a cat,' comes the reply. 'Next.'

'This one looks really lovely. A beautiful timber-framed house in Norfolk overlooking the sea. They've got two greyhounds and a whippet.'

'No, don't like the sound of that one. That's the North Sea you're talking about and it'll be December. Can you imagine taking a pack of dogs out on the beach in a howling gale? We'd freeze to death. No. Definitely not. Next.'

'Okay, well this is the only other one that I think fits the bill. It's a large country house in Northumberland with two chocolate labradors but one of them's a puppy. Apparently it's on an estate where there are the usual farm animals but we wouldn't need to have anything to do with them according to the advert. There's a farm manager and staff so our duties would only involve looking after the house and the dogs. It does look fabulous darling. Here, have a look at the photos.'

I hand Rob the iPad and lean over his shoulder while he scrolls through the details.

'Mmm. It does look wonderful. It's an amazing building and the dogs look lovely, especially the pup. What's his name?'

'Bertie.'

'Aw, he's cute. How old is he?'

'I think he's about a year. He'll have lost his baby teeth but he'll still be learning the basics.'

'Well that's okay, and the other dog'll help to keep him in order. What's he called?'

'He's actually a she, and she's called Bella.'

'It looks worth a go, but how on earth do we get there Chris? It's not an easy place to reach from here. It's no use applying if it's difficult to get to.'

'We could fly to Newcastle via Southampton and there's a vehicle included. I'm sure they'd come and collect us from the airport if we asked nicely. Anyhow, that's all hypothetical. We haven't got it yet.'

Having put an application together we're excited to receive a message to say that the owners would like a video call so that we can 'meet' each other before either of us accepting. So, date and time agreed, we settle ourselves on the sofa and wait for a Facetime alert. Sure enough, bang on six o'clock, the phone rings and we find ourselves face to face with an elderly couple sitting side by side on a settee, he ruddy-faced, bespectacled and balding, sitting with legs akimbo, she wearing a string of pearls and matching stud ear-rings, her grey hair swept back in a smart chignon.

'Good evening,' barks our host. 'Good to meet you folk. I'm Randolph,' he says taking a swig of what looks like whisky from a tumbler and waving at us. 'And this is my wife Lavinia,' he announces, turning and smiling at her.

'Hello,' growls Lavinia in a very low, masculine-sounding voice. 'Thanks awfully for this, we just thought it would be jolly useful to have a chat before we agreed anything.'

'Absolutely,' replies Rob. 'It's always good to get to know one another and find out what the duties involve. I'm Rob and this is my wife, Christine.'

'So you two have obviously done this sort of thing before,' says Randolph.

'Yes, we've been sitting for people for four years now so we've got a fair bit of experience,' replies Rob, nudging me with his leg.

'Any good at training puppies?' laughs Randolph, elbowing his wife in the ribs. 'Bertie's proving to be quite a handful, isn't he darling?'

'You could say that, but he is adorable and Bella's doing a jolly good job of sorting him out,' she replies.

'He looks really cute in the photos you put on the web-site,' I remark. 'How old is he now?'

'Only eight months but he's coming on a treat with his training, isn't he Randy?' says Lavinia, turning to her husband.

At this point Rob gives me an even heftier blow in the leg and I have to stifle a giggle.

'So when would you need us to arrive if we all decide to go ahead with this?' asks Rob.

'Well we'll need to be orf on the 17th, so if you can be here the day before it would give us a chance to show you the house and meet the dogs,' replies Lavinia, taking a drag on what looks like a small cigar. 'I think we mentioned the fact that we own the estate here but we've got a farm manager and other staff who'll take care of that side of things. My horses are stabled at the moment but George our manager will see to them.'

My ears prick up at the mention of horses.

'So do you ride?' I ask.

'Ha!' guffaws Randolph. 'Born in the saddle this gal. Still rides with the hunt don't you darling? There's no stopping her.'

I'm full of admiration for this lady who must be at least seventy. I certainly wouldn't have the courage to get out of second gear on a horse now.

'So how long have you lived there?' asks Rob.

'Only eight years and we're still working on the place,' replies Randolph. 'It was a wreck when we took it on but we got it for a song when the Duke started selling off some of his properties. It'll be a while before we have the ballroom and the servants' quarters habitable, but we'll get there.'

I can see Rob gulp as we both begin to appreciate the grandeur of the place.

'So where were you before you went to Northumberland?' I ask.

'Norfolk,' replies Randolph, 'just down the road from Sandringham in fact.'

'So what do you two reckon? You up to the challenge?' asks Lavinia, taking a sip from a long-stemmed glass.

I'm not so sure I like the word 'challenge' but clearly Rob has been lured.

'I'm sure we are, aren't we Chris?' he replies, turning to me with a huge smile.

'Er, yes, absolutely,' I agree.

'Great stuff!' beams Randolph taking another swig from his glass. 'In which case we'll get back on the web-site later this evening and confirm everything. Jolly nice chatting to you. Cheers and 'night both! Awfully good of you. We'll be in touch shortly.'

'Good night,' we chorus.

As soon as we're off line we both collapse into fits of laughter.

'Gosh, I never realised that there are still people who talk like that!' howls Rob. 'It seems we're jolly well orf to the wilds of Northumberland. I can't wait!'

The house stands on the crags just outside the small market town of Rothbury, an imposing building, but very much a crumbling pile. As Randolph pulls the BMW up the drive Lavinia appears at the door to greet us, the dogs at her heels barking furiously, obviously curious to meet their visitors.

'Hello. Welcome to God's country!' she calls from the top of the curving, stone staircase. 'Have you had a decent journey?'

'Yes, fine thank you,' I reply. 'What a wonderful place you have. It's such a beautiful setting.'

'Thank you. Yes, we love it here but we've got our work cut out. Probably be dead before we finish it, but we're determined to give it our best. Anyhow, come on in and I'll pour you a drink.'

As we climb the staircase to the front door I feel as though I'm on the set of Downton Abbey, but on a somewhat smaller scale. On entering the huge entrance hall I'm somewhat taken aback by the sight of a huge, stuffed bear, rearing up at the foot of a grand staircase that makes a gracious curve to the first floor. The poor beast looks sadly worn, his expressionless, glass eyes staring into the distance, paws raised as if to ward off an attacker. Lavinia notices me looking at it and quickly interjects,

'Oh, take no notice of him. Randy's been dragging him round for years from house to house. I'm surprised he hasn't fallen to bits. Bloody awful thing if you ask me.'

I have to quietly agree with her. The poor creature is quite grotesque and seems decidedly out of place in this day and age. I notice Bertie giving the beast a wide berth as he follows us through into the kitchen, his eyes keeping careful watch in case the bear lunges at us.

Nothing could have prepared us for the welcoming rural scene but there, standing with its rear end up against the Aga, is a Shetland pony.

'Charlie, get out at once!' bellows Lavinia. 'Out! Go on, out! How many times have I told you you may not come in the kitchen. He's a devil for this,' she sighs while frantically shooing

Charlie out of the kitchen in the direction of the back door. 'Now, out!' she bawls at him, giving him a hard slap on the rump, at which Charlie trots off hurriedly towards what appears to be the stable-yard beyond the house.

'You'll need to keep the back door shut or he'll appear out of nowhere,' she says apologetically. 'It's our own fault for letting him into the house when he was a baby. Now he thinks he has every right to join us in the kitchen. Just make sure you keep the bolt across the door if you're not around.'

Rob and I stare at each other, trying hard to suppress a fit of the giggles.

'Hopefully you won't have any incidents like that while we're away. He's a little bugger for sneaking in when your back's turned.'

The next morning, Lavinia and Randolph safely on their way, we decide to take a walk round our new home. Bella and Bertie join us, Bertie sinking his teeth into the legs of various pieces of furniture, gnawing quite seriously at the already decaying detail of various antiques, as we take in the extent of the house. The ballroom certainly classifies as work in progress, its wooden floor covered with water stains where the roof has leaked, the moulding on the plaster ceiling sadly yellowed and, in places, heavy window shutters hang on one hinge while others rest on the floor awaiting repair.

'Wow! This is going to be quite something when it's restored,' I call to Rob who's already staring out of the window at the landscape beyond.

The surrounding fields, separated from the house by a ha-ha, contain some magnificent trees. An avenue of copper beech leads into the distance, but next to the house sits a huge cedar, its branches almost brushing against the walls and occasionally stroking the windows. I can't resist waltzing around the room with my imaginary partner and envisaging what it must have been like when parties were held here.

'Gosh, it's even got a sprung floor Rob,' I comment as I feel the boards give beneath my feet as I move. 'Imagine the cost of restoring all this.'

'Well they must have a bob or two or they wouldn't have taken it on in the first place. According to Randolph they've got two and a half thousand acres, although a lot of that must be moorland round here, but there's a fair amount of forestry from what I can see. It's a huge project, that's for sure. Anyhow, let's go and explore.'

Bella ambles along dutifully by our side while Bertie leaps around making attempts at chewing her tail. A gentle, warning snap of her jaws and he's soon put in his place. I think her presence might be a godsend in helping us to keep him in order.

We walk down a long, narrow corridor hung with portraits of people we assume must be family, trying not to knock against any of the huge, china vases that tower over us, precariously balanced on what are obviously expensive antique tables and chests. I can already sense myself getting twitchy in case Rob manages to bring one crashing to the floor.

'Crikey, it's like visiting a National Trust property,' he remarks.

As the corridor opens out into a splendid sitting-room my eye falls on a grand piano, a Steinway, its top supporting a collection of photographs. It's only a matter of seconds before I recognise the framed faces and I give a shriek of excitement.

'Rob, come and look! They know the Royals!' I gasp.

Rob joins me and is clearly equally taken aback by the signed photos of not only Prince Charles and Camilla but by Prince Philip and the Queen herself.

'Good grief! We are moving in exalted circles Chris. I didn't realise that they were that important.'

'Maybe they rubbed shoulders when they lived in Norfolk,' I suggest. 'They might have been neighbours for all we know.

Come to think of it we don't even know their surname. They might even be extended members of the family.'

'We'd better be on best behaviour then. Do you fancy a cup of tea? It's already time for elevenses and then we can get these two out for their walk.'

At the mention of the W-A-L-K word Bella goes running back down the corridor towards the kitchen, swiftly followed by Bertie, who belts after her, skidding on the carpet runners, his tail thrashing from side to side. A couple of the tables judder as he passes.

'I think we're going to have to be extra-vigilant with the pup Rob or we'll have priceless pieces of china crashing to the floor. It might be a good idea to keep these two out of this part of the house and just restrict them to the kitchen.'

We spend the afternoon out on the estate with the dogs, exploring the farm and the surrounding land. The area seems absolutely vast compared to home but it's a joy to be able to let the dogs run freely. They gambol through the heather together, Bertie doing somersaults and leaping around like a spring lamb.

'Do you realise that this estate is a sixth of the size of our island?' announces Rob. 'Imagine what that would cost!'

'Yes, but all you can do here is grow trees or farm sheep. The moors can't support anything else and look at that line of crags over there. So much of the land here's redundant which is why it comes in cheap compared with home.'

It's just as we're heading back to the house when we notice a figure coming out of one of the farm buildings. It's a man wearing a flat cap and carrying a gun under his arm. Bella and Bertie rush off to greet him and he makes a fuss of them while waiting for us to approach.

'Afternoon,' he says, holding out his hand to welcome us. 'You must be the house-sitters. Lord Branscombe asked me to keep an eye out for you. Welcome to the estate,' he says warmly,

'Henry. I'm the game-keeper round here.'

'Nice to meet you,' replies Rob, shaking hands with him. 'I'm Rob and this is my wife Christine.'

'Hello, it's nice to meet you,' I reply. 'We were just trying to familiarise ourselves with the lay of the land.'

'Excuse me asking but is that a border accent?' asks Rob, his own soft burr seeming suddenly more evident.

'Northumbrian,' replies Henry, the 'br' of the word coming from somewhere at the back of his throat. 'Don't whatever you do suggest I'm a Geordie. They're a different breed,' he says, laughing.

'Well, you've certainly got your work cut out,' remarks Rob, looking around him at the huge expanse of land.

'You could say that, the forest alone's a full-time job. The deer are my department. Just keeping the numbers in check's enough. We need to make sure we've got a healthy population but at the same time protect the trees. We organise regular shoots throughout the season, but don't worry,' he smiles, recognising the slightly anxious look on my face, 'I'll let you know the dates. You'll need to keep these two indoors I'm afraid.'

'You mean there'll be shoots while we're here?' asks Rob.

'Yes, we've got a couple organised over the next few days. It's a popular venue and it brings in some income for the estate. Helps to pay my wages. Anyhow, I'd better get back to work. I'll see you two around,' at which he touches his cap and walks off in the direction of the office.

'Gosh, it's a different world up here Chris. I don't know how I feel about shooting. I suppose it's necessary sometimes but to do it for pleasure seems pretty grim. Oh, and what do you reckon to our Lord Branscombe. I'm assuming he was talking about Randy.'

'I suppose he must be. I didn't realise that we should have been bowing and scraping the other day. Anyhow, let's get these two home and have some lunch.'

Bella ambles into the kitchen and plonks herself down in her bed but Bertie's more interested in what we're having to eat and keeps launching himself at Rob, stuffing his nose in his trouser-pocket where he keeps the treats. No amount of firm commands is going to stop him from pestering us.

'I can only suggest that we put him outside Rob. We're never going to get any peace while we're eating. Why don't you tie him up outside and we'll let him back in when we've eaten?'

'Okay, good idea. Come on Bertie, you're getting kicked out. Nasty Aunty Christine doesn't love you.'

Bertie follows him out to the yard looking dejected where Rob tethers him to an iron ring in the wall of the house. As a consequence our lunch is accompanied by constant barking, whining and the sound of clawing against the kitchen door.

'This is fun,' shouts Rob, munching on his sandwich.

'Well how's about we put him in the ballroom and shut the doors. He can't get up to any mischief in there and according to Lavinia...'

'You mean Lady Branscombe,' interrupts Rob.

'Okay, according to Lady Branscombe he hasn't learned to climb the stairs yet so he'd be fine.'

'Right, I'll move him. Come on Bertie. Nasty Aunty Christine's had enough of you barking. You're going to be imprisoned instead. Don't worry Uncle Rob still loves you,' at which point I notice a treat making its way into Bertie's mouth.

'I saw that!' I shout. 'Stop trying to score points Mr Baird!'

Half an hour later, lunch eaten, it seems remarkably quiet.

'I'd better go and check on the boy,' says Rob. 'Maybe he was tired after our walk and he's having a kip.'

A few seconds later Rob's back with a big grin on his face.

'Come and see this Chris,' he says taking me by the hand and leading me towards the ballroom.

The room is empty but there, at the top of the adjoining staircase, is Bertie who has clearly managed to get himself up the stairs but obviously hasn't yet mastered the art of getting down. He's crying and looking dolefully down at us, desperate to be comforted. He stretches out a leg and puts his weight on his paw but quickly retracts it, clearly nervous at the idea of transferring his weight. Instead he turns sideways and lowers a hind leg gingerly down onto the next step but very quickly decides that that's a bit too dodgy. We watch as he attempts all sorts of creative manoeuvres but remains well and truly stuck.

'Oh bless him, I'd better go and rescue him,' says Rob.

'Is that a good idea darling? I know he's still a puppy but he's a big dog. Maybe we should do it together.'

'No, I'll be fine. It'll be more awkward with two of us. You hang on there and I'll get him down.'

I don't know what it is about Rob but he always feels like an accident waiting to happen. As he runs up the stairs two at a time I'm already anxiously anticipating the potentially perilous descent.

'Come on Bertie, down you come,' says Rob, taking him by the collar and patting the step immediately below him. 'You can do it.'

Bertie whines and plonks his bottom down firmly on the top step and looks imploringly at Rob.

'It's no use Chris, I'm going to have to pick him up and carry him.'

All I can do is turn my back. The sight of Rob teetering at the top of the stairs with 24 kilos of struggling dog in his arms is more than I can cope with.

'Right, got him,' I hear Rob call down to me. 'Come on Bertie, there's a good fellow.'

As I turn round I'm just in time to see Rob lose his footing and fall backwards onto the stairs. Man and dog somehow part company and Bertie comes slithering down the stairs head first like a chocolate waterfall, closely followed by Rob. By the time they reach the bottom I'm not sure which of them is the more bewildered by the experience. However, Bertie recovers quickly and is soon expressing his gratitude to his rescuer by licking Rob's face generously. Reassured that they're both still in one piece I burst into fits of laughter.

'Oh very funny! Thank you for your concern,' scowls Rob, trying to fight off Bertie. 'You do realise I could have broken something Chris.'

'I know but you haven't and that was just so funny,' I laugh, trying hard not to choke on my tears. 'I wish I'd had the phone on me to capture the moment.'

Dear Bella has come to investigate the rumpus and I just manage to catch hold of Bertie before he attempts to scale the stairs again to show off his latest accomplishment.

'Now we're going to have to confine him to the kitchen like it or not or he'll be able to wander around upstairs. This boy's becoming quite a challenge,' I sigh.

We've been given the task of administering some ear-drops to Bella who's had a bit of an infection, so each evening, after she's had her dinner, she sits dutifully while we squirt a couple of drops into each of her ears. A quick rub of each one afterwards and a treat to reward her and all's done. Bertie watches curiously, his head moving from side to side in puzzlement, then, as Bella moves off the rug he dutifully comes and sits in her place.

'Ha! I reckon he wants the same treatment so he can have a treat,' surmises Rob and so he pretends to give Bertie a squirt in each ear, rubs each side of his head and then dispenses a treat. Bertie jumps up, tail wagging, and heads off to find Bella.

'He is funny isn't he? He's going to be such a lovely dog when he grows up. I've really fallen for labs Chris. They have such a gentle nature and they're bright.'

'No, we are not, repeat not having another dog Rob. We've had this conversation so many times. Now how's about looking after me for a change and pouring me a glass of wine?'

It's past eleven o'clock when we settle the dogs down and head for bed, a rather grand four-poster with a decaying canopy and a lumpy mattress. There's a distinct smell of damp in the room and the occasional moth flutters up to the bed-side lamp.

'I feel as though I'm lying in state,' mumbles Rob from under the covers. 'I have to say it's not the most comfortable bed I've ever slept in. It must be horse-hair or whatever they used to use. I hope it doesn't do my back in.'

'Stop moaning and go to sleep,' I reply, turning onto my side and heaving some of the covers over me. 'Night night Mr Grumpy, sleep tight,' but my words are already drowned by Rob's gentle snoring.

The weather is becoming increasingly cold and the absence of any central heating in the house drives us to the comfort of the Aga. The four of us spend much of our time huddled together in the kitchen with blankets over our legs, only occasionally braving the biting cold in order to exercise the dogs. Christmas is fast approaching but as yet there's no sign of snow, although the water troughs in the yard have already been frozen over on several occasions. However, we take the precaution of driving into Rothbury to buy enough provisions to see us through in case the roads become impassible. I treat us to a turkey breast as a token gesture for Christmas Day and Rob insists on us buying a Christmas pudding and a tin of custard.

It's on the run-up to Christmas Eve that Rob develops his customary winter cold. Fortunately he's come prepared with echinacea and a box of Beecham's to help him through. There's a jar of honey in the pantry and I dose him up with hot milk and a generous teaspoonful.

'Mmmm. You can smell the heather in it Rob. It's wonderful. That'll make you better in no time,' I say reassuringly. 'They say that eating the local honey is one of the best things you can do for a cold.'

Clearly not convinced, Rob spends the next two days sniffling by the Aga with Bella lying on his feet. I'm left with the task of walking the dogs on my own but actually enjoy playing at being the lady of the manor. It's while I'm out one afternoon, my green wellies crunching in the frozen ruts left by the farm tractors, that I see Henry pulling up in his Landrover looking unusually agitated.

'Hi!' I shout. 'Everything okay? You look a bit fraught.'

'Sorry,' he replies. 'I'm afraid I've just had a pretty awful experience.'

'I'm sorry, anything I can help with?' I ask.

'No, no thanks, I just found myself in a really tricky situation. We've been getting calls from a few of the land-owners and villagers to say that there's a marauding stag in the area. He's been getting onto people's land and doing a lot of damage so I told the folk who'd rung to let me know if he turned up again. I got a call early this morning to say that he'd been seen not far from here just outside one of the local villages so I grabbed my kit and hot-footed it over in the Landrover. I found the house, grabbed my gun and went and knocked on the door only to be greeted by a man and his little girl. I guess she must have been about seven. The bloke was pleased to see me but when the little girl saw my rifle she looked up at him with tears rolling and asked him if I'd come to shoot Rudolph.'

'Oh my God, what did you do?' I gasp, imagining the horror of the situation.

'Well I could hardly go and put a bullet through his head under the circumstances so I turned round and came home. I'll just have to hope he makes his way into a more remote area but he's going to have to be shot I'm afraid.'

'Do you know, I've never seen deer in the wild,' I confess. 'It must be magical.'

'Oh it is, there's nothing more special than witnessing them in the forest just as the sun comes up. You'd be welcome to join me one morning if you want to but I do tend to leave while it's still dark. You'd have to set your alarm clock.'

'Oh I'd love to if you're sure that's okay,' I reply.

'Well how about tomorrow morning? I can drop by at about half six and pick you up if you're sure that's not too early.'

'No, don't worry, I'll be there. See you tomorrow then?' and I head back to the house with the dogs at my heels.

As I tell Rob about my plan for the morning I can see that he's still looking rough. The cold has settled on his chest and he's now developed a foul cough.

'I don't have to go love, I think I should be staying here to look after you.'

'I'll be fine. I'll only be asleep at that ungodly time anyhow. So long as you can take the dogs out when you get back.'

So the following morning I'm up and fumbling about in the dark waiting for Henry to pick me up. Bang on six thirty the headlights of the Landrover appear and he pulls up outside. A ten minute drive and we arrive at a pull-in where he parks the vehicle.

'I'll be with you in a minute,' he says, opening the back door of the vehicle. 'I just need to get my kit.' Then suddenly, 'Shit!'

'Problem?' I ask.

'I've forgotten the bloody torch, excuse my French,' he curses. 'I know the track like the back of my hand but you'll never cope unless,' he hesitates, 'unless you don't mind hanging onto me until we get to the platform?'

'I'll do whatever's needed, don't worry,' I reassure him.

And so, for what seems like an eternity, we make our way through the forest in the depths of an inky-black darkness, the likes of which I have never experienced. I recall being out in woodland when I was younger but there had always been the hint of the tree-line against the darkness of the sky when you looked up. This morning there is no hint. It's just black and it's as if I'm blind. I can't distinguish anything. My other senses kick in and my hearing becomes so acute it almost hurts. Grabbing hold of Henry's hand for guidance seems rather too intimate so I hang on to the sleeve of his waxed jacket instead. I'm aware of the twigs and branches snapping beneath our feet and our breathing, laboured with the effort of our walk. Suddenly we stop and Henry takes my hands and places each of them around two wooden poles. He leans into me and whispers,

'It's the ladder up to the seat, you're going to have to climb. It's only seven rungs and you're there.'

Gingerly I feel for the first rung with my foot and then count as I make my way up in the darkness, sensing a slight change in the light. I hold on tight to the framework, wondering just how precarious this platform actually is. Soon Henry is beside me and we stand side by side in silence, waiting for the dawn.

And when it comes it's breathtaking, the likes of which I've only ever seen in nature documentaries, as the sun begins to light up the forest and golden shafts of light start to radiate from behind the tall, upright trunks of some of the trees. The colours seem suddenly intense after the absence of light then, magically, a solitary deer appears, head upright and alert, its nose working over-time but its eyes steady. Henry leans towards me,

'You okay if I shoot her?' he whispers.

I simply wasn't prepared for this. I'd never imagined that he'd actually come equipped to kill. I thought we'd just come to watch the deer and now I'm faced with a split-second decision. I realise that this is of my making and that I should have expected it and pleading with him to let her go seems out of order. After all this is his work, he does this all the time. But not today I'm silently pleading. Please not today.

'Yes, okay,' I whisper, hardly believing that I've just said that.

I watch him lift the gun to his shoulder and take aim. He cocks the gun, but before I have time to reel at the horror of the situation, the doe is off, bounding through the undergrowth, the white of her tail disappearing until she's out of sight. I can't help but let my relief show.

'Sorry about that, I realise that I hadn't prepared you,' says Henry apologetically.

'No, no it's fine. Anyhow, she got away so let's not fret about it. It was magical and she was so beautiful. I hadn't realised they were so small.'

'Yes, the roe deer are, especially the females. Anyhow, let's get you back to base. You must be ready for some breakfast.'

I share my story with Rob on my return, who deservedly gets breakfast in bed.

'It was so stupid of me not to realise that he was out to shoot the poor creature. I can't get over my naïvety. Thank goodness she escaped because I don't know what I'd have done if he'd shot her.'

'Probably wept buckets and turned vegetarian,' replies Rob, munching on his toast. 'I don't think I'd have been able to say yes if he'd asked me.'

'Oh now you're making me feel even worse. We have to accept that this is the country. Hunting is part of people's lives here. We can't stroll in and ask them to change their ways. Anyhow, how are you feeling and how are the woofties?'

'I'm getting there slowly I think, although my throat's still a bit sore. But Bertie's acquired a new skill while you were out.'

'Oh, and dare I ask what that is?'

'He's turned into a doggy sommelier and has been helping himself to bottles of wine out of the wine rack downstairs.'

'Oh no, he hasn't broken any has he?'

'Not that I'm aware of, although he was very close to opening a bottle of Sancerre. We'll have to put a barrier of some sort across the rack to stop him. I imagine that some of those wines could be pretty expensive and I certainly don't want to have to replace them.'

It's Christmas Eve by the time Rob has recovered from his cold.

The sky looks heavy with snow and the clouds above the crags have turned a dramatic, leaden grey. I'm quietly hoping that we get a heavy snowfall as the landscape will be transformed. It's while I'm dreaming of a winter wonderland that there's a loud knock at the door. I recognise Henry's voice above the barking of the dogs who have turned up to greet him.

'Good morning,' he says, removing his cap with a flourish. 'Delivery for Mr and Mrs Baird,' he announces, handing me a bottle of champagne and a small package. 'The bottle's courtesy of Lord and Lady Branscombe and that's from me,' he says, pointing to the parcel. 'It's a fillet of venison. I thought you might enjoy it over Christmas.'

'Oh thank you so much Henry that's so kind of you and wow, champers! We really are living in style.'

'Well, Merry Christmas. I'm off duty now for a few days and I'm hoping to get home before this lot comes down,' he says, pointing up at the clouds.

'Of course, and a Merry Christmas to you too Henry. And thank you for the other morning, it was very special.'

He turns and smiles and heads back to the farm, his hand waving above his head.

'Crikey,' says Rob when he sees the bottle on the table. 'Dom Perignon! Where's that come from? I trust Bertie hasn't been helping himself from the wine rack again?'

'No, it's a present for us from Randolph and Lavinia. Isn't that kind of them? Oh, and Henry called by with this too,' I say, showing Rob the contents of the parcel.

'Gosh, that looks wonderful. But I assume it's venison? Are you going to be able to eat it after your little adventure?'

'D'you know I'm not really sure. I'm finding it really hard not to relate a cut of meat to an animal after seeing that deer. At this rate it'll be nut roast for Christmas dinner.'

We wake the following morning to a pristine blanket of snow.

The scene outside is like a Christmas card. When I open the door the dogs rush out and bound around playing, Bella behaving like an overgrown puppy. It's obviously Bertie's first experience of snow and he keeps taking great mouthfuls and then shaking his head at the shock. Suddenly there's a loud whinny and Charlie arrives out of the blue, trotting briskly towards the kitchen door.

'Quick! Shut the door before he gets in!' I shout to Rob.

We both make a bee-line for the door, crash into one another and end up sitting on our backsides while the dogs climb on top of us, tails wagging, and attempt to lick our faces.

'Well this is going to be a memorable Christmas if ever there was one,' I laugh.

It's while I'm preparing the evening's dinner that a cry comes through from the sitting-room where Rob has settled down to watch the television.

'Chris,' he calls.

'What is it? I'm busy.'

Rob appears hurriedly at the door.

'Have you any idea where Randolph and Lavinia were going for Christmas?'

'Yes, they said they were going to stay with friends in Norfolk near to where they used to live. Why?'

'Quick, come and see,' he says grabbing me by the arm and dragging me through to the sitting-room where the news is on.

'There, look!' he says excitedly, pointing at the TV. 'I thought it was them!'

Sure enough, as the cameras focus on the members of the Royal Family gathering on the steps of Sandringham Church, there in the background are the unmistakable figures of Randolph and Lavinia.

'Oh my God!' I cry with excitement. 'You're right Rob. It's definitely them. Oh my goodness, you don't suppose they're staying with the Queen do you?'

'Who knows? But we can pretend. That'll impress your sister!'

'Too right! We can dine out on that one for a while. Ha! The Queen. Oh my!'

Just before we sit down to dinner Rob pops the champagne cork and, after carefully pouring two glasses of bubbly, we chink glasses.

'Merry Christmas darling,' he says happily. 'And thank you for all that you've done this year, dragging me round the country. I wonder where we'll be this time next year? Anyhow, we've got twelve months to fill before then and no doubt you'll manage to find some more adventures for us.'

'Well actually,' I smile sweetly...

# ACKNOWLEDGEMENTS

BARKING MAD WOULD NEVER have come about without the generosity and friendship of the many owners who have let us share their homes and lives since we began house-sitting. Whilst the episodes in the book have been inspired by some of the adventures that we have had, the owners, animals and houses are purely fictitious with the exception of those featured in Chapter 1.

We were unprepared for the affection that we very quickly felt when looking after other people's furry families and will always fondly remember the many animals that we have had the privilege to care for.

On the human front I would like to give particular thanks to Steve Foote of Blue Ormer Publishing for helping me to put this book together; to Iain Welch for his wonderful illustrations; to Peter Kenny, Laura Sheridan, Barbara, Simon and Kay for being my sounding-boards while I was writing it, and especially to my husband, Richard, who would like it to be known that, other than writing poetry and mending things with super-glue, in no way does he resemble Rob. Without his continuous help and encouragement my stories might well have remained in a notebook.

My thanks also to the wonderful extended family of the Twittersphere whose camaraderie, love for animals, compassion and support for others makes the world a better place.

My special thanks go to our special furry twitterpals: Rhodry the princely, Scottish deerhound, star of *Victoria* and *Gentleman Jack*; Rex the TV terrier handsome aficionado of fine sticks; the adorable Rumplepimple; our lovable, great pal Bertie Lakeland; and our very special friend, Scheggia.

Jane Mosse 2020

# ABOUT THE AUTHOR

Jane Mosse was born in Newcastle-Upon-Tyne where she was awarded the title of Freeman of the City and, as a result, has the right to graze her cow on the town moor. She began her writing career as a researcher and writer for *Nicholson's Guide to the Waterways* alongside developing her love of poetry. In 2018 she published her first collection of poems, *Guernsey Legends*, in partnership with local artist Frances Lemmon.

*Barking Mad* is her first novel and was inspired by some of the adventures that she and her husband Richard have had since taking up house-sitting following their retirement. They live on the beautiful island of Guernsey in the Channel Islands.

Iain Welch is an artist and illustrator living in rural North Herefordshire. He spends most of his time drawing, walking and cuddling dogs.

More information about him can be found at iainwelch. co.uk.

'I am a terrier on a mission. When I was asked to sniff this book I leapt at the chance. If you love dogs and people who love us grab this book with all four paws. Share it with your humans too. They'll pawsitively love reading about dog sitters and their adventures. Books with dog stories help the world see that dogs are family too. Licks and puppy dog kisses.'

Rumplepimple @Rumplepimple1

'Mum loved this book. A fun read about pet sitters Chris and Rob and the adventures they had in lots of different places with all sorts of animals. I would love Chris and Rob to come and look after me!'

Rhodry @DeerhoundRhodry

'As a logophile, I enjoy a good book. And as a dog, it was only idonious that I would read a book about two intrepid caregivers of canines (and felines as well). This charming tale is both full of jocularity as well as dramaturgy, the misadventures and quiet moments of caring for the beloved pets of complete strangers. As fascinating as I found the zoosophy, I found the insights of anthroposophy even more compelling. Thoroughly enjoyable and entertaining reading.'

Rex @rexthetvterrier

'As a young flourishing Lakeland Terrier I feel very honoured to have been able to follow the progress of this lovely book since an early stage. Enjoy reading it and take a moment to view it all through a dog's eyes.'

Bertie Lakeland @bertie_lakeland